ASSESSMENT AND TREATMENT OF ANXIETY DISORDERS IN PERSONS WITH MENTAL RETARDATION

Edited by

ANN R. POINDEXTER, M.D.

NADD NATIONAL ASSOCIATION for the DUALLY DIAGNOSED
— Mental Illness/Mental Retardation

TABLE OF CONTENTS

SERIES FOREWORD

The books in this series, published annually, present the newest developments in a specific area of concern. Each book will contain a balance of chapters reporting theoretical formulation, empirical research, clinical procedure, and models of service delivery. In most instances, the chapters represent a combination of NADD-sponsored conference presentations and invited papers edited by a topic editor selected specifically for each book.

As Series Editors, we look forward to a successful series of books that keep us informed of advances in knowledge and practice.

Series Editors:

Robert J. Fletcher, D.S.W., A.C.S.W.
Executive Director
National Association for the Dually Diagnosed
Kingston, NY

William I. Gardner, Ph.D.
Professor
Rehabilitation Psychology Program
University of Wisconsin-Madison
Madison, WI

CONTRIBUTORS

Lark Kirchner, R.N., M.S.W.
Department of Psychiatry
Southern Illinois University
School of Medicine
P. O. Box 19230
Springfield, IL 62794-9230

Earl L. Loschen, M.D.
Chair, Department of Psychiatry
Southern Illinois University
School of Medicine
P. O. Box 19230
Springfield, IL 62794-9230

Robert J. Pary, M.D.
Department of Psychiatry
Southern Illinois University
School of Medicine
P. O. Box 19230
Springfield, IL 62794-9230

Ann R. Poindexter, M.D.
Health Care Management
Consultant
1024 Clifton Street
Conway, AR 72032

Steven Reiss, Ph.D.
Nisonger Center University
Affiliated Program
Ohio State University
1581 Dodd Drive
Columbus, OH 43210-1296

Peter B. Rosenquist, M.D.
Department of Psychiatry
Wake Forest University
Bowman Gray School of
Medicine
Medical Center Boulevard
Winston-Salem, NC 27157

Ruth M. Ryan, M.D.
Developmental Disability
Program
Public Psychiatry
4200 East 9th Avenue
Denver, CO 80262

Catherine A. Saliga, L.C.S.W.
Department of Psychiatry
Southern Illinois University
School of Medicine
P. O. Box 19230
Springfield, IL 62794-9230

ASSESSMENT AND TREATMENT OF ANXIETY DISORDERS IN PERSONS WITH MENTAL RETARDATION

Anxiety disorders are extremely common in the general population—experts state that the typical primary care physician sees at least one individual every day with an anxiety disorder. Anxiety disorders are more common than diabetes mellitus in the primary care office (McGlynn & Metcalf, 1989). Reiss in 1994 pointed out conflicting evidence concerning the overall rate of anxiety disorders in persons with mental retardation. He cites references reporting prevalence rates from very low to rates at least comparable to those for the general population. Since many symptoms of anxiety disorders concern subjective feelings, the difficulties in communication experienced by individuals with mental retardation and other developmental disabilities may contribute to under-reporting and subsequent undertreatment of these conditions. In 1994 King and his group reported descriptive data of 251 institutionalized individuals consecutively referred for initial psychiatric consultation from a large group of persons with predominately severe to profound mental retardation. While they noted the heavy reliance of diagnostic criteria on the individual's ability to describe the subjective symptoms of anxiety, they still found that 12% of the individuals referred to them had constellations of signs and symptoms that were best captured in the anxiety disorder spectrum.

Because of the apparent frequency of these conditions, wide-spread interest in the topic, and a relative lack of written material on the topic, the National Association for the Dually Diagnosed (Mental Health/Mental Retardation) (N.A.D.D.) developed an N.A.D.D.-A.A.M.R. preconference symposium on "Evaluation and Management of Anxiety Disorders in Persons with Mental Retardation," presented on May 30,

1995 in San Francisco, California at the national meeting of the American Association on Mental Retardation. This monograph was developed from material from that symposium, additional chapters on related topics, and diagnostic criteria for common anxiety disorders as described in <u>Diagnostic and Statistical Manual of Mental Disorders, Fourth Edition, (DSM-IV)</u> (1994), the latter used with permission from the American Psychiatric Association.

Two initial chapters of this monograph concern the incidence of anxiety disorders in a specialized referral clinic for persons with developmental disabilities, as well as a discussion of anxiety disorders in elderly persons with mental retardation.

The next chapters concern specific anxiety disorders, obsessive-compulsive disorder (O.C.D.) and post-traumatic stress disorder, which are of particular interest to those who serve a population of persons with mental retardation and related disabilities. The chapter on O.C.D. discusses tic disorders also, since both conditions relate to complex repetitive movements, which are commonly seen in this population.

One chapter discusses nonpharmacologic modalities of treatment.

Another chapter discusses some issues related to research in the area of anxiety disorders. Since diagnosis of anxiety disorders in persons with mental retardation often rests heavily on reports from knowledgeable observers, the final chapter of this monograph discusses methods of training of direct support staff and other interdisciplinary team members in these issues.

The monograph appendix contains diagnostic criteria for commonly seen anxiety disorders, as outlined in <u>DSM-IV</u>. This information is listed by permission from the American Psychiatric Association. Also included in the appendix is a self-directed instructional training program for interdisciplinary team members. While all of the material contained in the monograph is protected by copyright, this training program (<u>only</u>) may be copied and used for training as needed.

This monograph editor and the NADD monograph series editors hope that you will find this information helpful as you work with individuals with developmental disabilities.

Monograph Editor: Ann R. Poindexter, M.D.

References

American Psychiatric Association. (1994). *Diagnostic and statistical manual of mental disorders* (4th ed.). Washington, DC: Author.

King, B. H., DeAntonio, C., McCracken, J. T., Forness, S. R., & Ackerland, V. (1994). Psychiatric consultation in severe and profound mental retardation. *American Journal of Psychiatry, 151,* 1802-1808.

McGlynn, T. J. & Metcalf, H. L. (Eds.) (1989). *Diagnosis and treatment of anxiety disorders: A physician's handbook.* Washington, DC: American Psychiatric Press.

Reiss, S. (1994). *Handbook of challenging behavior: Mental health aspects of mental retardation.* Worthington, OH: IDS Publishing.

ANXIETY DISORDERS IN A CLINIC POPULATION

E. L. LOSCHEN, M.D.

CATHERINE A. SALIGA, L.C.S.W.

Southern Illinois University School of Medicine

Anxiety disorders are among the most common of psychiatric disorders in the general population, yet little is known about the incidence of these disorders in persons with developmental disabilities (Ollendick, T.H. & Ollendick, 1982). Now, more than ever, it is critical to make specific diagnoses of psychiatric disorders, because of the advent of efficacious treatments that are more and more specific in their application. In light of the heavy use of neuroleptic medications in the population of persons with mental retardation, it is even more important to accurately diagnose conditions for which there are known treatments with fewer long-term risks to the person being treated.

Craft (1959) found no persons with a diagnosis of neurosis in his review of inpatients at an institution for persons with mental retardation. On the other hand, King, DeAntonio, McCracken, Forness, and Ackerland (1994) reviewed their findings on 251 consecutively referred patients in a center for persons with developmental disabilities. Reasons for referral were classified into six groups. Within these groups the occurrence of anxiety disorders ranked third and varied from 11% to 25%, with only the diagnostic groups of stereotypy/habit disorder and impulse control disorder being found more commonly.

Several studies have looked at the occurrence of anxiety disorders in clinic populations. Craft (1960) found approximately 11% of 119 referrals of persons with mental retardation to an outpatient clinic at Maudsley to have a co-existing problem with anxiety states. In a study of 100 consecutive outpatients, Philips and Williams (1975) did not report anxiety disorders separately, but noted that anxiety reactions were a frequent concomitant of other diagnoses. Neurotic disorders were, however, diagnosed in 23.8% of the 62 children evaluated as having non-psychotic disorders. In a psychiatric outpatient clinic for children with mental retardation, Reid (1980) found 22% of the sixty children evaluated to have a neurotic diagnosis. Benson (1985) surveyed 130 children and adults with developmental disabilities seen in an outpatient mental health clinic and discovered that 25% of the individuals evaluated were diagnosed as either conduct or anxious-withdrawal disorders. These diagnoses were noted to be more common in persons with the milder level of intellectual impairment. The results of her study do not allow for separation of these two classes of disorders, so the prevalence of anxiety disorders in this population cannot be precisely stated. Finally, a recent study (Bouras & Drummond, 1992) found that 6.6% of community residents referred to a specialty developmental disability clinic had a diagnosis of anxiety disorder using criteria from DSM-III.

Ultimately of most interest to us is the prevalence of a disorder in a community setting. Although sparse, some data do exist for this for anxiety disorders in persons with developmental disabilities. Jacobson (1990) reviewed diagnostic and demographic data on the 42,479 persons with developmental disabilities contained in the New York data base that has been in operation since 1979. This data base contains all persons who have been identified in the state as having a developmental disability, and therefore allows a very close approximation of a total community sample. He found that the prevalence of neurotic disorders in persons age 21 and less (using DSM-II nomenclature) was 1.32%, and for persons 22 and older, 1.49%. Of course, DSM-II diagnoses of neurosis contained several groups of diagnoses not now included with the anxiety disorders, such as depressive neurosis and hysterical neurosis, so that the prevalence of anxiety disorders in this population would undoubtedly be less than the numbers indicated above. Richardson, Katz, Koller, McLaren, and Rubinstein (1979) found that 26% of young mentally retarded adults in a comprehensive survey of an English community were thought to have experienced neurotic disorders. This number again would include a number of conditions in addition to anxiety disorders. In a study using DSM-III-R criteria, a survey of all adults over age fifty with learning disabilities in a single district in the United Kingdom found a prevalence of 15.2% of all psychiatric disorders, of which 5.7% represented anxiety disorders (Patel, Goldberg, & Moss., 1993). A major strength of this study is the use of clearly defined criteria and the use of structured and computerized methods of obtaining a diagnosis.

Consequently, no clear picture of the prevalence of anxiety disorders in persons with mental retardation emerges from the literature. It is apparent, however, if a more accurate diagnosis of anxiety disorder can be made in persons with challenging behavior, such persons can potentially be spared the risks of more general, non-specific treatments such as neuroleptics, that carry much higher risks than some of the newer treatment approaches to anxiety disorders.

The Special Needs Clinic

We have provided a clinic (Special Needs Clinic—S.N.C.) for persons with developmental disabilities and challenging behavior at Southern Illinois University School of Medicine for the past decade. The clinic meets for two half-days each week, and is variously staffed with two psychiatrists with extensive experience in treating persons with dual diagnosis, two social workers, a psychologist, psychiatric residents, medical students, and intermittently with trainees from other mental health professions. Most referrals to the clinic are of persons with mental retardation who also exhibit severe challenging behavior, including aggression towards others or property or self-injurious behavior. Most referrals come from community programs, but a substantial number of persons living in institutional settings are also seen. People are seen for evaluation, consultation, and, in many instances, long-term psychiatric treatment and follow-up. The clinic is in its third year of collecting and recording a variety of demographic and clinical information on all persons served in the clinic. This data base is being developed both for administrative reasons and to serve as a research tool.

The S.N.C. has an established protocol for collecting clinical information on all persons referred to the clinic for evaluation. Prior to the formal psychiatric evaluation a series of instruments, questionnaires, and other clinical/administrative information is requested from the referral source and caregivers. Records are requested of the most recent physical examination, laboratory studies, previous hospitalizations, medical history, and medical consultations to establish a medical baseline, since often medical conditions may precipitate disturbed behavior, especially in non-verbal persons. We also obtain reports of any psychological tests and social histories which are available. We request the referral source to complete a medication history, which attempts to get a complete history of the use of psychotropic drugs for the person being evaluated. We ask program personnel to complete and return to us for scoring the Reiss Screen and Aberrant Behavior Checklist. In addition, either the P.I.M.R.A. or the D.A.S.H. is requested, depending on the person's level of intellectual impairment. Once this information has been received, and a formal psychiatric evaluation, including a formal mental status examination, has been completed, other structured instruments are utilized, depending on the presenting complaints and other critical variables. These latter instruments are always individualized for the person being evaluated.

Since the database for the S.N.C. has been established, 267 unduplicated persons have been seen at Southern Illinois University School of Medicine in the Division of Developmental Disabilities. Men evaluated outnumber women by 159 to 108. The age range of persons seen is from nine to 76, with an average of 37 years. The population is predominantly Caucasian (86.5%), with 12% African-American and 1.5% all others.

Diagnoses are included in the database only when the clinical team feels confident that the relevant diagnostic criteria from DSM-IV have been met sufficiently to merit the diagnosis. Psychiatric diagnoses are therefore quite conservative, and many of the individuals being served are classified non-specifically, as either stereotypic movement disorder with self-injurious behavior or as impulse control disorder not otherwise specified, until such time as the team is comfortable making a psychiatric diagnosis. Of the persons in this population 72 have been given the diagnosis of either impulse control disorder not otherwise specified or stereotypic movement disorder. We use these diagnoses in our clinic for persons who present with aggression or self-injurious behavior and for whom no specific Axis I diagnosis has been established. We anticipate that a portion of these individuals represent undiagnosed conditions while in other instances these represent basically behavioral disorders with or without organic overlay. Because of this of this very conservative diagnostic approach, only 21, or approximately eight percent, of persons in the database have received a diagnosis of an anxiety disorder. This may also reflect that referrals to the S.N.C. are usually quite severely impaired and pose major management problems, leading to a predominance of either psychotic, affective, or behaviorally disturbed individuals in the group.

The 21 individuals with anxiety disorders represent a spectrum of disorders. Obsessive-compulsive disorder (O.C.D.) represents the largest subgroup, with nine persons with this diagnosis. We have been careful to not include persons with autism in this category, since in most instances of autism it is quite difficult to demonstrate the active resistance of the persons to the obsessions or compulsions as required in the diagnostic criteria in DSM-IV. One person in this (O.C.D.) group also carries a secondary diagnosis of post-traumatic stress disorder.Generalized anxiety disorder or other anxiety disorder represents the second largest group, seven individuals. Post-traumatic stress disorder was diagnosed in four individuals and one person was identified as having panic disorder. Four of these individuals are not receiving psychotropic or anticonvulsant medications at present. Not all 21 individuals are presently receiving psychiatric follow-up in the S.N.C., and some are new to S.N.C., therefore the present medication regimens do not necessarily represent in our view the best practice of treatment. Several persons are in the process of being slowly tapered off neuroleptic medication, with ten persons still receiving these drugs. For those patients receiving services in the S.N.C., we have a goal to eliminate neuroleptic medication in all instances except those in which psychotic symptoms can be clearly demonstrated.

Of the nine persons with a diagnosis of O.C.D., two are being successfully treated with selective seratonin reuptake inhibitors (S.S.R.I.s) and one person is on no medication. One person is receiving risperidone, while two others are receiving typical neuroleptic medications. The other three persons are receiving anticonvulsant medication or lithium carbonate. Of all the medications prescribed, only the selective seratonin reuptake inhibitors have a clearly established rationale for use, and consequently continued efforts to simplify the psychopharmacologic approach are underway.

Persons with generalized anxiety disorder or other anxiety disorder were likewise found to be receiving treatment with a variety of medications at the time of evaluation, including neuroleptics, buspirone, benzodiazepines, or anticonvulsants. One person in the group now is not receiving psychotropic medications but is being treated with group psychotherapy. Of the four persons with a diagnosis of post-traumatic stress disorder, two are not receiving medications, while one is on an anticonvulsant and the other a neuroleptic and S.S.R.I. combination. The person with panic disorder is on a combination of anti-anxiety and neuroleptic drugs.

Of the 21 persons with anxiety disorders, five are known to be receiving group psychotherapy. Of these five individuals, three are also receiving individual psychotherapy. One other person is receiving individual psychotherapy in addition to medication. This represents a developing focus of our clinical services, in that we encourage the use of psychotherapeutic approaches to persons with dual diagnoses in all cases where the person is able to participate in such a treatment and a clear treatment focus can be identified. We have not found I.Q. or "psychological mindedness" to be useful parameters in judging who can profitably benefit from such treatment.

Case Example

A case example from our clinic may prove informative to illustrate some of the aspects of anxiety disorders and our approach to evaluation. This 36 year old woman presents with a history of aggression and multiple crying episodes. Her major complaint is the occurrence of episodes of apparent panic in which she often states, "I am scared!" She is classified as being moderately mentally retarded, although her performance is probably significantly impaired by her inability to concentrate on tasks. Her aggression usually occurs in close proximity to her episodes of crying and general discomfort. She has long been noted to prefer the company of staff rather than peers. For several years she has indicated that she has been sexually abused by her father, and subsequent protective intervention has assured that he does not have contact with her. Her episodes are usually spontaneous, with no clear precipitating factors or situations noted by staff. She has been on neuroleptic medication for fifteen years, and is now on a slow tapering program to eliminate this class of drugs. She receives lithium carbonate with little evidence of response, and likewise has been tried on buspirone and trazadone. Over all, she is now more stable in the past, although little credit for this can be attributed to the psychopharmacologic approach up to the time of her present regimen. She has recently been started on sertraline as a specific treatment for panic disorder and the immediate response has been promising.

She has received a variety of evaluations which are both intriguing and informative. The Reiss Screen is positive for a dual diagnosis with items of impulsive, temper tantrums, anxious, attention seeking, and dependent being rated as 1.5 or above. Items rated as 1.0 or above include aggressive, fearful, over sensitive, body stress, and low energy. These items closely approximate diagnostic criteria for anxiety. Some support for this comes from one administration of the Hamilton Anxiety Rating Scale, in which she received a score of 29, although a later administration only found a score of seven. D.A.S.H. items for anxiety, depression, mania, and impulse control were among those noted to be elevated.

References

Benson, B. A. (1985). Behavior disorders and mental retardation: Associations with age, sex, and level of functioning in an outpatient clinic sample. *Applied Research in Mental Retardation, 6,* 79-85.

Bouras, N. & Drummond, C. (1992). Behaviour and psychiatric disorders of people with mental handicaps living in the community. *Journal of Intellectual Disability Research, 36,* 349-357.

Craft, M. (1959). Mental disorder in the defective: A psychiatric survey among in-patients. *American Journal on Mental Deficiency, 63,* 829-834.

Craft, M. (1960). Mental disorder in a series of English out-patient defectives. *American Journal on Mental Deficiency, 64,* 718-724.

Jacobson, J. W. (1990). Do some mental disorders occur less frequently among persons with mental retardation?. *American Journal on Mental Retardation, 6,* 596-602.

King, B. H., DeAntonio, C., McCracken, J. T., Forness, S. R., & Ackerland, V. (1994). Psychiatric consultation in severe and profound mental retardation. *American Journal of Psychiatry, 151,* 1802-1808.

Ollendick, T. H. & Ollendick, D. G. (1982). Anxiety disorders. In J. L. Matson & R. P. Barrett (Eds.), *Psychopathology in the mentally retarded* (pp. 77-119). New York: Grune & Stratton.

Patel, P., Goldberg, D., & Moss, S. (1993). Psychiatric morbidity in older people with moderate and severe learning disability: II: The prevalence study. *British Journal of Psychiatry, 163,* 481-491.

Philips, I. & Williams, N. (1975). Psychopathology and mental retardation: A study of 100 mentally retarded children: I. Psychopathology. *American Journal of Psychiatry, 132,* 1265-1271.

Reid, A. H. (1980). Psychiatric disorders in mentally handicapped children: A clinical and follow-up study. *Journal on Mental Deficiency Research, 24,* 287-298.

ANXIETY DISORDERS IN ELDERLY PERSONS WITH MENTAL RETARDATION

ROBERT J. PARY, M.D.

A recent review concluded that anxiety disorders are probably more prevalent in persons with mental retardation than in the general population, but there are "more questions than answers" (Ollendick, T. H., Oswald, & Ollendick, 1993). The authors cite only one prospective study regarding anxiety disorders and persons with mental retardation, and that study was in young adults. It appears safe to believe that there are even fewer answers and many more questions about anxiety disorders in elderly persons with mental retardation. Nevertheless, this chapter will review six areas pertinent to anxiety disorders in older persons with mental retardation. The first three sections will summarize anxiety disorders in the general population; a) overview of anxiety disorders, b) primary anxiety disorders among elderly individuals, and c) secondary anxiety disorders among elderly persons. The last three sections will focus on persons with mental retardation: d) difficulties in diagnosing anxiety disorders in persons with mental retardation, e) approaches for diagnosing anxiety disorders in elderly individuals with mental retardation, and f) treatment implications.

Anxiety Disorders in the General Population

The Epidemiologic Catchment Area (E.C.A.) survey found that anxiety disorders are the most prevalent of the major psychiatric disorders (Regier et al., 1988). The most common anxiety disorder is social phobia. Social phobia is probably the least severe disorder in this category, but the other anxiety disorders are often associated with significant morbidity (Ballenger, 1991). During any month, 7.3% of the population probably have a diagnosable anxiety disorder. The lifetime risk for an anxiety disorder is about one in seven people, 14.6% (Regier et al., 1988). Unfortunately, the E.C.A. survey excluded individuals with mental retardation. According to the E.C.A. data, anxiety disorders peaked between 25-44 years (8.3%). The disorders became less common as people got older. Of those 45-64 and 65 and older, 6.6% and 5.5%, respectively, had anxiety disorders. Brickman and Eisdorfer (1989) hypothesize why reports of anxiety disorders might be lower in elderly persons. In one study, older men acted in an experimental learning setting as if they were anxious, but did no experience anxiety symptoms. Therefore, these subjects might deny suffering from anxiety when surveyed. Brickman and Eisdorder (1989) offer other suggestions to account for the lower incidence of anxiety such as cognitive impairment may reduce the ability to remember stressful stimuli and individuals with more trait anxiety may have either died or become institutionalized prior to age 65.

Primary Anxiety Disorders Among Elderly Individuals in the General Population

Although the E.C.A. data found that the prevalence of anxiety disorders decreased with age, phobias were still the second most frequent psychiatric disorder next to cognitive impairment in persons over 64 years of age. Apparently the phobias of old age were of new onset, and not merely the graying of phobic individuals whose illness began in their twenties or thirties (Eaton et al., 1989; Lindesay, Briggs, & Murphy, 1989). Older persons may appear agoraphobic because they fear crime. Surveys of elderly persons found a lower perception of safety in their neighborhoods than younger individuals. This fear of victimization may lead to a restriction of mobility (Stein, 1988).

The E.C.A. research is not the only epidemiologic study of anxiety disorders among the elderly. Flint (1994) reviewed eight random-community surveys, including the E.C.A. study, of anxiety disorders in persons sixty and older, and found considerable variability. Rates ranged from 0.7% to 18.6%. Nevertheless, from one-tenth to one-fifth of community-dwelling elderly seek medical attention for anxiety symptoms (Myers, Weissman, & Tischsler, 1984). Furthermore, nearly twenty percent of elderly will be prescribed antianxiety drugs in any given year (Sherrill, Colenda, & Reifler, 1994).

One criticism of the E.C.A. survey and pertinent to the other six random-community surveys is that rates of psychiatric disorders are not listed for the subgroup of elderly residing in institutions (Bland, Newman, &

Orn, 1988). This criticism seems particularly meaningful as one tries to extract information from the general population and apply it to a developmentally disabled population which has a higher percentage of institutionalized persons. Bland and group (1988) conducted 3258 diagnostic interview schedules (D.I.S.) evaluations in Edmonton, 199 of these with individuals in nursing home/auxiliary hospital beds. This comprised 6.1% of the sample, in contrast to the 7.7% of elderly persons in Edmonton who are in institutions. This institutionalized population was compared to 358 elderly living in households, and provided some interesting contrasts. Nearly twice as many elderly males living in the community had an anxiety disorder as did those living in an institution (2.7% versus 1.4%, respectively). The difference occurred because 1.8% of community-dwelling males had phobias, versus none of those in institutions. The rate of obsessive-compulsive disorder (O.C.D.) was slightly higher in institutionalized males than in those in the community (1.4% versus 0.9%). Phobias were over twice as common in elderly women living in the community than those living in institutions (3.8% versus 1.6%). Nevertheless, elderly institutionalized women had more anxiety disorders than those in the community (7.1% vs. 4.1%). The increase in anxiety among institutionalized women was mainly due to panic disorder (1.6% vs 0.5%) and O.C.D. (4.7% vs. 1.9%).

The increase in panic disorder among institutionalized women is not due to a new onset of primary disease. Unlike phobias, primary panic disorder or primary generalized anxiety disorder (G.A.D.) rarely begin in the elderly. One needs to strongly consider that a panic disorder or G.A.D. may be secondary to depression or to a medical disorder if those conditions present for the first time after age sixty. The issue of a new onset of O.C.D. in the elderly is unclear. One study (Eaton et al., 1989) found that the prevalence of O.C.D. in males steadily decreased from the third decade (0.66%) to the seventh decade (0.12%). Findings are different in females. Compared to the 45-64 year group, elderly women had a slight increased prevalence of O.C.D..

There are no published surveys of the prevalence of post-traumatic stress disorder (P.T.S.D.) in elderly individuals in the general population (Flint, 1994). This is of potential significance for persons with mental retardation. Ryan (1994) believes that persons with mental retardation are at greater risk for P.T.S.D.. She found 16.5% of 310 consecutive evaluations of referred persons with developmental disabilities had diagnosable P.T.S.D.. The prevalence of P.T.S.D. among elderly persons with mental retardation, however, is virtually unknown.

Comorbid anxiety and depression may occur. From one-third to one-half of depressed elderly individuals, both inpatients and outpatients, presented with moderate to severe symptoms of anxiety, according to a presentation made by Mulsant at the annual conference of the Anxiety Disorders Association of America ("Depression-Related Anxiety," 1995). Generalized anxiety disorders were excluded, but the other comorbid anxiety disorders were unexpectedly low. Only 3% to 5% had current anxiety disorders, and only 8% to 9% had a lifetime history of anxiety disorders.

Bereavement is another condition in which a mixture of depression and anxiety occurs, although anxiety can predominate (Brown, et.al., 1991).

Secondary Anxiety Disorders Among Elderly Individuals

The term secondary anxiety disorder refers to anxiety that is caused by a medication or a medical illness. Secondary anxiety becomes of increasing importance to the elderly because of the large number of substances and physical disorders that can cause anxiety (Brown et al., 1991). Intoxication from illicit substances such as amphetamines, hallucinogens, and cocaine is less a problem in the elderly than in younger individuals. Intoxication from other substances, however, may cause anxiety symptoms. These substances, all available over-the counter, include anticholinergics, caffeine, steroids, and sympathomimetics. Withdrawal from alcohol, narcotics, sedative hypnotics, and tobacco may all lead to anxiety. Tobacco withdrawal may be especially important because of the number of programs that limit the number of cigarettes, though there is little objective evidence that smoking reduction programs actually increase behavioral symptoms.

Brown et al. (1991) provide a comprehensive list of medical illnesses that can cause anxiety. They divided the illnesses into three categories: neurologic, cardiovascular/respiratory, and endocrine/metabolic. Neurologic illnesses that can manifest as anxiety are delirium, complex partial seizures, akathisia, and vestibular dysfunction. Of these disorders, elderly persons with mental retardation may be prone to delirium. The key to suspecting delirium is recognizing the fluctuating levels of consciousness that accompany the fear and anxiety. Complex partial seizures may present with intense fear and feelings of unreality, as well as accompanying diaphoresis, flushing, hyperventilation and tachycardia. Tardive akathisia has been reported after long-term use of neuroleptics. A large number of elderly persons with mental retardation who receive neuroleptics and have akathisia, which is a sense of internal restlessness leading to an inability to sit still, may be confused with having anxiety.

Several cardiovascular/respiratory conditions are associated with anxiety, including mitral valve prolapse, hypoxia, cardiac arrhythmias, angina, myocardial infarction, congestive heart failure, pulmonary edema, pulmonary embolism, and chronic obstructive pulmonary disease.

Endocrine/metabolic conditions associated with anxiety include acid-base imbalance, hypoglycemia, Cushing's syndrome, hyperthyroidism, hypocalcemia, pheochromocytoma, and carcinoid syndrome.

Difficulties in Diagnosing Anxiety Disorders in Persons with Mental Retardation

The following case history illustrates some of the difficulties in diagnosing anxiety disorders in elderly individuals with mental retardation. Ms. A. was a 66-year old woman who lived at a developmental center. The chief complaint was "the patient once in a while becomes extremely agitated, talks a lot—and this has been going on for almost a year." Also, last year she started complaining of chest pain, and there appeared to be a circular effect between her chest pain and anxiety. When she had chest pain she became anxious and hyperventilated, but anxiety increased her chest pain.

Twice within six months prior to the evaluation, she was hospitalized for chest pain. The work-up was negative except for an echocardiogram showing concentric left ventricular hypertrophy, bicuspid aortic valve with mild to moderate calcified aortic stenosis, and slight mitral annular calcification. She has been diagnosed with cardiomegaly and congestive heart failure. Her medications included Cardizem 90 mgm every eight hours, Zantac 150 mgm twice a day, one nitroglycerin patch daily, and furosemide 40 mgm/day.

She answered most of the initial evaluator's question of how she was doing by saying, "It hurts, it hurts." Her problems included frequent complaints of chest pain and many somatic complaints. On the Reiss screen, scales above the cutoff were aggressive behavior and dependent personality. These findings were described as most consistent with a diagnostic indication of behavior problem, adjustment problem, antisocial personal-

25

ity disorder, or personality disorder. Nevertheless, when the individual items on the Reiss were examined, Ms. A. met DSM criteria for an anxiety disorder. Anxiety and hostility (irritability) were considered major problems. She also had a problem with a sleep disturbance, and was inattentive and easily fatigued. She was placed on Buspirone 10 mgm three times a day, and has remained stable at 24 month follow-up.

This case illustrates several problems in diagnosing anxiety disorders in elderly individuals. First, the chief complaint was not anxiety, but extreme agitation. Second, she met criteria on only once screen, PIMRA, for an anxiety disorder, and that was not the primary diagnosis. Third, the diagnosis was made, in part, by analyzing raw data from the screening instruments. Fourth, her anxiety disorder was probably not primary, but secondary to her medical condition.

Diagnosing Anxiety Disorders in Elderly Persons with Mental Retardation

Ideally, this would be the section of this chapter to review all of the research on anxiety disorders in elderly persons with mental retardation. Unfortunately, a MEDLINE literature search through 1994 failed to find any such studies. The only pertinent reference found was one case (Case #3, Mr. C.) described in an article discussing use of buspirone in individuals with developmental disabilities (Ratey, Sovner, Mikkelsen, & Chmielinski, 1989). Mr. C. was a 63-year old individual with profound mental retardation. Three days after his workshop closed he manifested denudative behavior, reversal of self-care skills, decreased appetite, insomnia, ritualistic behaviors, and aggression, the latter in the form of swearing, biting, hitting, and property destruction. Although his initial diagnosis was agitated depression, with both affective and anxiety symptoms, the decision was made to treat his anxiety symptoms with buspirone. After two weeks his dose was 30 mgm/day. After five to seven weeks Mr. C.'s symptoms dramatically decreased. This case has some limitations, since the trial was not double blinded and there were no rating scale measures of anxiety symptoms. Also, a spontaneous remission of an adjustment disorder with disturbances of mood cannot be ruled out using the available data.

Although very little information exists in the developmental disabilities literature to guide clinicians, several steps may assist diagnosis of anxiety disorders in elderly persons with mental retardation. The first step is to determine if anxiety exists. This may not be obvious, especially if physical aggression or self-injurious behaviors predominate. The second step is determination of whether the anxiety should be considered abnormal, since not everyone with anxiety has an anxiety disorder. Sometimes anxiety is an appropriate reaction. For persons who become anxious because of severe harassment, treatment of "anxiety disorder" would not be appropriate. Assuming that the anxiety is not reasonable given the circumstance, the third step is determination of whether or not the symptoms are secondary to a physical illness, as hyperthyroidism, or to medications, as akathisia. The fourth step is determination of whether or not the anxiousness is due to environmental or psychosocial stressors, such as overcrowding or excessive noise. The fifth step should involve analysis of whether the anxiety symptoms fit with other symptoms into a DSM-IV disorder.

Treatment Implications

Review of all nonpharmacologic and pharmacologic interventions is beyond the scope of this chapter. Some information on these topics is included elsewhere in this book. In brief, treatment should be aimed at the basic pathophysiologic abnormality underlying anxiety disorders. For elderly persons whose anxiety is secondary to a medical problems such as hyperthyroidism or angina, treatment should be relatively straightforward—correct the medical problem. Unfortunately, as with Ms. A., an exclusive focus on her cardiomegaly and angina was not enough. She still required an anxiolytic drug. Treatment should be directed at attempting to remove or modify the noxious stress.

The treatment plan for primary anxiety disorders can be divided into nonpharmacologic and, if needed, pharmacologic approaches. Before reviewing the nonpharmacologic and pharmacologic approaches it may be useful to consider two of the many theories of anxiety. The adrenergic dysregulation model of Abelson and Cameron (1994) proposes that anxious persons may be excessively vigilant in scanning the environment for threat, may become overly aroused once threat is perceived, and/or may get overly "defensive" (avoidant) once aroused. Alternatively, some individuals fear actually developing anxiety (Reiss, 1991). These individuals believe something catastrophic will happen if they feel anxious.

In the first, adrenergic dysregulation, model, teaching a person relaxation exercises to use in situations and/or using an anxiolytic drug when the person is excessively vigilant may be therapeutic. In this case the emphasis is on reducing the physical signs of arousal. Furthermore, determination that an individual is hypervigilant can be made regardless of his/her intellectual functioning. The model can include a person's cognitive set—what the person thinks about the perceived threat may alter the adrenergic "gain"—but could conceivably focus merely on the dysregulation of the adrenergic receptors.

In the second model the emphasis is on the cognition. Here, a problem-solving skills training program may be beneficial (Benson, 1995). As an example, suppose an individual fears that he/she will lose all control while riding a bus. The intervention involves teaching the person that even if they become nervous during the during the bus ride, they do not lose control. If, however, the person is unable to communicate the fear that something catastrophic might occur, then this second model is not testable. Utilization of a problem-solving approach implies that the individual has the capacity to determine who they should turn to for help, what they should say (communicate), and when the problem will be solved (Benson, 1995).

References

Abelson, J. L. & Cameron, O. G. (1994). Adrenergic dysfunction in anxiety disorders. In O. G. Cameron (ed.), *Adrenergic Dysfunction and Psychobiology.* pp.403-446. Washington, DC: American Psychiatric Press.

Ballenger, J. C. (1991). Update on anxiety disorders. *Archives of Internal Medicine, 151,* 857-859.

Benson, B. (1995). Problem solving skills training. *Habilitative Mental Health Care Newsletter, 14,* 13-17.

Bland, R. C., Newman, S. C., & Orn, H. (1988). Prevalence of psychiatric disorders in the elderly in Edmonton. *Acta Psychiatrica Scandinavia, 77,* (suppl. 338), 57-63.

Brickman, A. L. & Eisdorfer, C. (1989). Anxiety in the elderly. In E. W. Busse & D. G. Blazer (Eds.), *Geriatric Psychiatry*, pp. 415-427. Washington, DC: American Psychiatric Press.

Brown, C. S., Rakel, R. E., Wells, B. G., Downs, J. M., & Akiskal, H. S.

(1991). A practical update on anxiety disorders and their pharmacologic treatment. *Archives of Internal Medicine, 151,* 873-884.

Depression-related anxiety may wane with age. (1995). *Clinical Psychiatry News,* p. 5.

Eaton, W. W., Kramer, M., Anthony, J. C., Dryman, A., Shapiro, S. & Locke, B. Z. (1989). The incidence of specific DIS/DSM-III mental disorders: Data from the N.I.M.H. Epidemiologic Catchment Area program. *Acta Psychiatrica Scandinavia, 79,* 163-178.

Flint, A. J. (1994). Epidemiology and comorbidity of anxiety disorders in the elderly. *American Journal of Psychiatry, 151,* 640-649.

Lindesay, J., Briggs, K., & Murphy, E. (1989). The Guy's/Age Concern Survey: Prevalence rates of cognitive impairment, depression, and anxiety in an urban elderly community. *British Journal of Psychiatry, 155,* 317-329.

Myers, J. K., Weissman, M. M., & Tischsler, G. L. (1984). Six month prevalence of psychiatric disorders in three communities 1980-1982. *Archives of General Psychiatry, 41,* 959-967.

Ollendick, T. H., Oswald, D. P., & Ollendick, D. G. (1983). Anxiety disorders in mentally retarded persons. In J. L. Matson & R. P. Barrett (Eds.), *Psychopathology in the mentally retarded, 2nd edition,* pp. 41-85. Needham Heights, MA: Allyn & Bacon.

Ratey, J. J., Sovner, R., Mikkelsen, E., & Chmielinski, H. E. (1989). Buspirone therapy for maladaptive behavior and anxiety in developmentally disabled persons. *Journal of Clinical Psychiatry, 50,* 382-384.

Regier, D. A., Boyd, J. H., Burke, J. D., Rae, D. S., Myers, J. K., Kramer, M., Robins, L. N., George, L. K., Karno, M., & Locke, B. Z. (1988). One-month prevalence of mental disorders in the United States. *Archives of General Psychiatry, 45,* 977-986.

Reiss, S. (1991). Expectancy model of fear, anxiety, and panic. *Clinical Psychology Review, 11,* 141-153.

Ryan, R. (1994). Posttraumatic stress disorder in persons with developmental disabilities. *Community Mental Health Journal, 30,* 45-54.

Sherrill, K. A., Colenda, C. C., Reifler, B. V. (1994). Psychopharmacology and psychotherapy. In W. R. Howard, E. L. Bierman, J. P. Blass, W. H. Ettinger, & J. B. Halter (Eds.), *Principles of geriatric medicine and gerontology, 3rd edition,* pp. 1137-1145. New York: McGraw-Hill.

TOURETTE SYNDROME AND OBSESSIVE COMPULSIVE DISORDER: TREATABLE CAUSES OF COMPLEX REPETITIVE MOVEMENTS IN MENTAL RETARDATION/ DEVELOPMENTAL DISABILITY

PETER B. ROSENQUIST, M.D.

Introduction

Complex repetitive movements and speech are pervasive and easily observable in persons with mental retardation and developmental disability (M.R./D.D.). Classification of these behaviors has proceeded simultaneously along phenomenologic as well as functional behavioral dimensions, leading to considerable terminologic confusion. Depending upon the training of the observer, and the setting in which it occurs, the same motor behavior (e.g. nose picking or eye rubbing) may be characterized as "habit," "self-injury," "self-stimulation," "stereotypy," "mannerism," "autism," "perseveration," "tic," "compulsion," or "ritual." In cases where systematic observations of motor behavior were not made prior to treatment with neuroleptics, differential diagnosis is further compounded by the so-called "tardive" syndromes. Without the "gold standard" of reliable patient self-report, the most basic differentiation between what is voluntary or involuntary is at best an exercise in probability.

Whatever they are called, complex repetitive movements have long been thought to interfere with social-adaptive behavior (Koegel & Covert, 1972). Unfortunately, lacking an accepted approach for diagnosis and management, clinicians often accept these behaviors as "par for the course," and concentrate on other treatment issues. However, two closely related disorders, Tourette Syndrome (T.S.) and Obsessive Compulsive Disorder (O.C.D.), may be important considerations when complex repetitive behavior is observed, since management of these conditions continues to evolve.

Tourette Syndrome

Tourette syndrome is named for Georges Gilles de la Tourette, who provided one of the early descriptions of this disorder which is characterized by simple and complex motor and vocal tics. A simple tic is a more or less involuntary rapid contraction or spasm of a group of muscles. A simple tic is essentially without purpose. Complex motor and vocal tics are generally slower, and may appear purposeful, although they are still considered involuntary. Some examples of complex motor tics are repetitive touching of objects and people, squatting, deep knee bends, retracing steps, twirling, nose twitches, grimaces, eye blinks, self-injury, and head banging. Complex vocal tics often involve grunts, barks, echolalia (repeating the statements of others), palilalia (repeating one's own statement), coprolalia (shouting obscenities), throat-clearing, stuttering, screams, yelps, and snorts. This condition affects approximately 100,000 people in the United States, with lifetime prevalence estimates between 0.5% and 1.6% (Shapiro, A. K., Shapiro, Young, & Feinberg, 1987).

Obsessive Compulsive Disorder

As the name implies, O.C.D. is characterized by obsessions (repetitive, intrusive thoughts) or compulsions (repetitive and often ritualistic behaviors performed purposefully to ward off harm or to neutralize the distress caused by obsessions). Some examples of compulsions include those behaviors involving excessive grooming or cleaning, ordering or arranging of objects, repetitive opening and closing of doors, clothes changing, hoarding of objects, touching, tapping, counting, or repeated "checking up" on some aspect of the individual or the environment. While O.C.D. was once considered a rare condition, data from the Epidemiologic Catchment Area (E.C.A.) and subsequent large scale studies estimate point prevalence between 1%-2% and lifetime prevalence in the range of 2.5%.

Differential Diagnosis

While the prevailing psychiatric nosology (now DSM-IV) classifies T. S. as a tic disorder and O.C.D. with the anxiety disorders, current evidence suggests they are related. Some individuals meet criteria for both disorders, and the same movement can conceivably be classified under either condition. Discrimination is particularly difficult between a complex motor tic and a compulsion (as repetitive touching) in persons who are unable to reliably communicate obsessions nor the purposefulness of the behavior. This is often the case with non-verbal persons with mental retardation. Differential diagnosis is further complicated by the fact that both O.C.D. and T.S. begin in childhood or adolescence, wax and wane over time, and are exacerbated during periods of stress or anxiety. Some evidence exists for shared genetic inheritance between T.S. and O.C.D., and intriguing links have also been demonstrated between these disorders and attention deficit disorder, other anxiety disorders, and major depression.

Tourette Syndrome in Mental Retardation

Although T.S. has motivated much research within the past twenty years, it is still under-recognized in the general population. Far less attention has been directed toward T.S. in the field of mental retardation. Nevertheless, at least twelve cases have been reported documenting Tourette syndrome in the M.R./D.D. population, associated with a range of conditions including Down syndrome (Collacott & Ismail, 1988), fragile-X syndrome (Kerbeshian, Burd, & Marsolf, 1984), XYY syndrome (Merkskey, 1974), and XXX with 9p mosaicism (Singh, Howe, Jordan, & Hara, 1982). Cases have been described with T.S. occurring comorbidly with M.R./D.D. presumed secondary to intrauterine and perinatal injuries (Golden & Greenhill, 1981). T.S. has been observed at all levels of intellectual and adaptive functioning.

A review of T.S. symptoms described in the literature documents a similar pattern for M.R./D.D. and general T.S. populations. Vocal tics in M.R./D.D. are predictably skewed toward simple meaningless sounds, given the language impairments in this population. Complex tics in the form of neutral phrases and complete sentences have not been reported. However, coprolalia and echolalia were reported in six and three cases, respectively. simple motor tics were reported in all but one M.R./D.D. case, with all muscle groups represented. The most common manifestations were head jerking, six cases, and eye blinking and shoulder shrugging, five cases each. Complex motor tics were present in ten cases, with a principal example of repeated touching of self, objects, and other persons, five cases. Touching has also been considered a compulsive behavior, a possible manifestation of O.C.D.. There is one reported case of aggressive and of self-injurious complex tics, and a third case in which these coexisted. This link deserves closer study in M.R./D.D. populations, considering the high prevalence of self-injury and aggression.

Treatment of Tourette Syndrome

Symptoms of Tourette syndrome wax and wane by nature. Of T.S. subjects treated with placebo alone, approximately equal percentages will improve, worsen, and remain unchanged (Shapiro, A.K., & Shapiro, 1988). A number of interventions have been proposed to alleviate the symptoms of T.S., although objective evidence for efficacy is limited, and for the M.R./D.D. population, entirely anecdotal. Behavioral techniques employed in the treatment of T.S. with nonretarded populations include contingency management (Varni, Boyd, & Cataldo, 1978), self-monitoring with feedback, and anxiety management. Effectiveness of these techniques is questionable, and a number of cases of treatment failure have been reported. Pharmacologic interventions used to treat T.S. have included various neuroleptics, clonidine, clonazepam, and a large number of less extensively studied agents including lithium, carbamazepine, nicotine, cannabinoids, and calcium channel blockers. Neuroleptics are the most widely used agents, especially haloperidol and pimozide, which have received F.D.A. approval for this indication. Reported improvement with this class of medications has varied from 62% to 91%. Withdrawal emergent effects include tardive dyskinesia and dystonia. With up to 75% of individuals experiencing significant side effects, some have questioned the appropriateness of treating all but the most severely affected patients (Erenberg, 1992). Clonidine, marketed as an antihypertensive agent, has been used in the treatment of T.S. since 1979, and has a less noxious side effect profile as compared to the neuroleptics. Effectiveness has not yet been fully established, however, since eight of 13 open trials, but only one of four blinded studies have demonstrated improvement for greater than 50% of subjects treated (Goetz, 1992).

Ten cases have been reported of comorbid T.S. and M.R./D.D. for which treatment has been specified. Five of eight patients treated with haloperidol were felt to be improved, as were two patients treated with pimozide and one treated with thioridazine. One of the persons who eventually responded to pimozide had worsening of tics when treated with clonidine. Extrapyramidal symptoms (akinesia, oculogyria, torticollis) occurred in four patients treated with haloperidol and both patients taking pimozide, although these were alleviated in most instances on addition of an anticholinergic agent. One patient was treated with a cue-controlled relaxation procedure both alone and in conduction with pharmacotherapy. While the procedure was helpful and reduced tics during active relaxation exercises, there was no generalization to the rest of the day for this person (Zarkowska, Crawley, & Locke, 1989). Together, these cases suggest a need for further study, employing standardized instruments, with a larger cohort.

Obsessive-Compulsive Disorder

Vitiello, Spreat, and Behar (1989) found ten cases of compulsive behavior consistent with O.C.D. in a sample of 283 residents of a facility for individuals with mild to profound mental retardation. The level of mental retardation in this group was evenly distributed between mild, severe, and profound levels. Of sixteen recorded behaviors in this group, six involved ordering compulsions, three checking compulsions, two cleaning, and two touching compulsions. Interrater reliability in this study was good (kappa = 0.82) for differentiating compulsions from "stereotypies" such as rocking, banging, flipping, and swinging objects and pleasurable behaviors such as verbal perseveration, humming, demanding attention, stealing, pacing, masturbation, compulsive eating, drinking, or smoking. The compulsive rituals were noted to cause significant disruption, including aggression toward interfering staff. A nine-item severity score developed for this study indicated significantly more impairment for patients with compulsive behaviors compared with M.R./D.D. controls.

The DSM-IV concept of obsessive compulsive disorder specifies that compulsions are in response to obsessive thoughts, and that the individual recognizes the actions are excessive or unreasonable. Because of the inherent limitations in determining these factors in the M.R./D.D. population, Gedye (1992) has proposed a rating scale based on 25 observable compulsive behaviors grouped under five types—ordering, completeness/incompleteness, cleaning/tidiness, checking/touching, and deviant grooming compulsions. This instrument, the Compulsive Behavior Checklist, further rates severity according to the extent of interference with daily living and response to staff interruption of compulsions. Fifteen subjects with developmental disability diagnosed with O.C.D. by DSM-III-R criteria were studied with this instrument. The number of individual compulsions ranged from eight to twenty, with a mean of 13 compulsions for each subject. Gedye found the range of these behaviors to be remarkably broad, with all 15 subjects having at least one compulsion in the categories of ordering, completeness, and leaning, 13 subjects with entries in four categories, and ten with entries in all five categories. The greater number and types of compulsions in this study as compared with the Vitiello sample may reflect selection bias, but may also be the result of systematic observation intended with a checklist methodology. The significance of compulsive behaviors is borne out in this sample, where compulsions took up more than an hour each day and interfered in most cases with daily routine, social activities, and/or relationships. As yet, no further data have been published regarding reliability and validity of this instrument, but it appears to be the most complete inventory available for characterizing compulsive behaviors and it is simple to administer.

Treatment of Obsessive-Compulsive Disorder

Clinicians have both behavioral and pharmacologic treatment options for managing obsessive-compulsive disorder in the general population. Behavioral techniques seem to be most effective for certain types of O.C.D. symptoms, particularly cleaning or checking rituals (Baer & Minichiello, 1990), and depend upon the patient being exposed to situations which trigger compulsive behavior and actively inhibiting the tendency to engage in the behavior. Pharmacologic efficacy in the treatment of O.C.D. has been well established in double-blind studies for clomipramine, fluvoxamine, fluoxetine, and sertraline. Studies are underway for paroxetine. These agents are thought to act be inhibiting the reuptake of serotonin into synaptic nerve terminals. While clomipramine may be slightly more effective than the others, it is more frequently associated with anticholinergic and antiadrenergic adverse effects (Jenike, 1992). Other agents used solely and adjunctively with variable success include monoamine oxidase inhibitors, benzodiazepines, lithium, buspirone, carbamazepine, and neuroleptics.

Behavioral treatment for O.C.D. in M.R./D.D. has been very little studied, but anecdotal success has been reported for various modalities including differential reinforcement of other behavior (D.R.O.), overcorrection, modeling, and performance feedback, which together reduced clothes checking and body touching in three mildly retarded men (Matson, 1982). In another case, D.R.O. procedure in combination with graduated in vivo exposure, relaxation, and physical interruption failed to attenuate compulsive handwashing (McNally & Clamari, 1989). This latter patient was unresponsive to treatment with amitriptyline as well, although thioridazine 25 mg. t.i.d. reduced somewhat the severity of her rituals. Two patients with O.C.D. (cleaning and checking behaviors), borderline mental retardation and adaptive functioning in the retarded range were treated with neuroleptics with similar modest improvement. Subsequent treatment with fluoxetine (20 mg. and 80 mg.) reduced Leyton Obsessional Inventory scores and improved performances in the industrial workshop.

Two recent open label studies have addressed the pharmacologic treatment of O.C.D. in the presence of the additional diagnosis of autism. McDougle, Price, and Volkmar (1992) report improvement in four of five individuals treated with clomipramine, as measured by the Aberrant Behavior Checklist (A.B.C.) and Clinical Global Impressions Scale (C.G.I.). Repetitive behaviors were typically reduced, accompanied by increased socially appropriate responding. Adverse effects were not reported for this study. Cook, Rowlett, Jaselskis, and Leventhal (1992) studied the effects of fluoxetine upon C.G.I. ratings of overall improvement and also a combined C.G.I. rating of perseverations, compulsions, or rituals in subjects with a utistic disorder (A.D.), and those with M.R. but not A.D.. Their results indicate improvement in global C.G.I. for 15 of 23 A.D. subjects and ten of 16 M.R. subjects. C.G.I. ratings of perseverations compulsions, and rituals were significantly reduced for the entire A.D. group compared to baseline, and a similar, nonsignificant trend was noted for the M.R. group. However, the baseline rating of perseverations, compulsions, and rituals did not predict response to fluoxetine for either group. Only three patients in the combined group were felt to meet criteria for O.C.D.—two A.D. fluoxetine responders and one M.R. nonresponder. Overall, nine of 39 subjects had side effects which significantly interfered with function or were felt to outweigh therapeutic effects. Most commonly reported side effects were hyperactivity/restlessness/agitation, insomnia, elated affect, and decreased appetite.

In summary, the literature substantiates that O.C.D. and T.S. are identifiable causes of complex repetitive movements in M.R./D.D. populations. Both conditions have been linked to aggressive and self-injurious behavior, as well as attention deficit and affective illness. Controlled studies are lacking, and differentiation between compulsions and complex tics is problematic. Nevertheless, a sufficient enough array of treatment options exists for these conditions to warrant clinical trials for those individuals who have tics or compulsions which interfere with optimal adaptive functioning.

References

Baer, L. & Minichiello, W. E. (1990). Behavioral treatment for obsessive-compulsive disorder. In R. Noyes, Jr., M. Roth, & G. D. Burrows (Eds.), *Handbook of anxiety, volume 4: The treatment of anxiety*, pp.363-387. Amsterdam.

Collacott, R. A. & Ismail, I. A. (1988). Tourettism in a patient with Down's syndrome. *Journal of Mental Deficiency Research, 32*, 163-166.

Cook, E. H., Rowlett, R., Jaselskis, C., & Leventhal, B. L. (1992). Fluoxetine treatment of children and adults with autistic disorder and mental retardation. *Journal of the American Academy of Child and Adolescent Psychiatry, 31*, 739-745.

Erenburg, G. (1992). Treatment of Tourette syndrome with neuroleptic drugs. In T. N. Chase, A. J. Friedhoff, & D. J. Cohen (Eds.), *Advances in neurology*. New York: Raven Press.

Gedeye, A. (1992). Recognizing obsessive-compulsive disorder in clients with developmental disabilities. *The Habilitative Mental Healthcare Newsletter, 11*, 73-77.

Goetz, C. G. (1992). Clonidine and clonazepam in Tourette syndrome. In T. N. Chase, A. J. Friedhoff, & D. J. Cohen (Eds.), *Advances in neurology*. New York: Raven Press.

Golden, G. S. & Greenhill, L. (1981). Tourette syndrome in mentally retarded children. *Mental Retardation, 19*, 17-19.

Jenike, M. A. (1992). Pharmacologic treatment of O.C.D. in obsessive disorder. *Psychiatric Clinics of North America, 15*, 895-919.

Kerbeshian, J., Burd, L., & Marsolf, J. (1984). Fragile-X syndrome associated with Tourette symptomatology. *Developmental and Behavioral Pediatrics, 5*, 201-203.

Koegel, R. L. & Covert, A. (1972). The relationship of self-stimulation to learning in autistic children. *Journal of Applied Behavior Analysis, 5*, 381-387.

Matson, J. L. (1982). Treating obsessive-compulsive behavior in mentally retarded adults. *Behavior Modification, 6*, 551-567.

McDougle, C. J., Price, L. H., & Volkmar, F. R. (1992). Clomipramine in autism: Preliminary evidence of efficacy. *Journal of the American Academy of Child and Adolescent Psychiatry, 31*, 746-750.

McNally, R. J. & Calamari, J. E. (1989). Obsessive-compulsive disorder in a mentally retarded woman. *British Journal of Psychiatry, 155*, 116-117.

Merkskey, H. (1974). A case of multiple tics with vocalization and XYY karyotype. *British Journal of Psychiatry, 125*, 593.

Shapiro, A. K., Shapiro, E., Young, J. G., & Feinberg, T. E. (1987). *Gilles de la Tourette syndrome, Edition 2.* New York: Raven Press.

Shapiro, A. K. & Shapiro, E. (1988). Treatment of tic disorders with haloperidol. In D. J. Cohen, R. D. Bruun, & J. F. Leckman, *Tourette's syndrome and tic disorders.* New York: John Wiley & Sons.

Singh, D. N., Howe, G. L., Jordan, H. W., & Hara, S. (1982). Tourette's syndrome in a black woman associated with triple-X and 9p mosaicism. *Journal of the National Medical Association, 74*, 675-682.

Varni, J. W., Boyd, E. F., & Cataldo, M. F. (1978). Self-monitoring, external reinforcement and time-out procedures in the control of high rate tic behaviors in a hyperactive child. *Journal of Behavior Therapy and Experimental Psychiatry, 9*: 353-358.

Vitiello, B., Spreat, S., & Behar, D. (1989). Obsessive-compulsive disorder in mentally retarded patients. *Journal of Nervous and Mental Disease, 177*: 232-236.

Zarkowska, E., Crawley, B., & Locke, J. (1989). A behavioral intervention for Gilles de la Tourette syndrome in a severely mentally handicapped girl. *Journal of Mental Deficiency Research, 33*: 245-253.

POST-TRAUMATIC STRESS DISORDER IN PERSONS WITH DEVELOPMENTAL DISABILITIES

RUTH RYAN, M.D.

Persons with developmental disabilities are exposed to trauma and abuse more frequently than other people (Sobsey, 1994; Blatt, 1970; Blatt & Kaplan, 1966). Exposure to trauma can alter the action of neurotransmitter systems, causing physiologic changes. These changes can influence almost every part of a person's emotional experience. Exposure to trauma can also alter learning patterns, leading to changes in expectations of and interactions with other people. Often the person is not fully aware that some of their reactions toward the world are reactions to past events. Because of the subtleties of context and extremes of the actual behavior there may be a variety of reactions from staff and other providers, who see only behavior and do not see context. Sequelae of unresolved trauma may include alterations in mood only, simple phobias, persistent non-useful learned patterns of interaction with others ("neuroses" in older terminology), or physical problems, as a higher frequency of autoimmune, endocrine, and neoplastic conditions. A small subset of people exposed to trauma experience posttraumatic stress disorder (P.T.S.D.), an especially complex anxiety disorder.

The <u>Diagnostic and Statistical Manual of Mental Disorders, fourth edition (DSM-IV)</u> (1994) criteria, paraphrased, for P.T.S.D. include:

A. Exposure to trauma that is extremely painful or life-threatening.

B. Persistent re-experiencing of the event through flashbacks (re-experiencing a major portion of the event with a visual memory of the event), partial flashbacks (re-experiencing a part of the event, such as the physical sensations of the trauma, without necessarily knowing this is what is being experienced), intrusive memories, and nightmares.

C. Persistent avoidance of stimuli associated with the event. This might include amnesia, refusal to participate in activities, feeling detached or estranged from others, sense of foreshortened future, restricted range of affect, voluntary dissociation, and phobias.

D. Persistent symptoms of arousal. This is the reason this disorder is classified as an anxiety disorder. The person is constantly tense and aware of the position of others. Other manifestations include sleep disturbance, problems concentrating, easy startle, and exaggerated emotional reactions to minor stimuli.

E. Duration of symptoms more than one month.

F. Clinically significant distress.

Because trauma and abuse are so often discovered in the histories of people with developmental disabilities, there may be a tendency to move from the discovery of trauma to the diagnosis of P.T.S.D.. Clearly there are many sequelae of trauma. Whatever sequelae are present must be accurately diagnosed so that an effective treatment program can be developed. For example, if an individual has only conflicted relationships with others as a sequela of trauma, but does not have all the other symptoms of P.T.S.D., then the persons may only require psychotherapy and not the rest of a P.T.S.D. protocol. For a diagnosis of P.T.S.D. to be made it is important that the individual actually meet the criteria.

The trauma criteria are, tragically, easily met. Sometimes the obstacle to recognition and documentation of these criteria is the resistance of those close to the person to the idea that such horrific things could occur, and that they would be perpetrated against people so unable to defend themselves.

Illustrative Case #1: S. T. is a 37-year old woman with an uncertain level of cognitive impairment who was referred for evaluation of "crazy talk," fighting, and screaming. She had a diagnosis of schizophrenia, although the only symptom thought to substantiate this was her "acting out non-reality-based scenes." These included cowering and screaming, as well as episodes of "acting out" scenes of experiencing sexual assault. She had no evidence of other symptoms of schizophrenia. Accompanying symptoms including hypervigilance (jumping with minor noises), phobias about certain rooms, wearing multiple layers to sleep, sleeping underneath her bed, waking up screaming several times per night, and occasional self-mutilation (carving sixes and crosses into her skin). In her drawings she showed numerous "satanic" symbols, rituals which involved sex with corpses, burning of other people, beatings, and drugging. She stated she believed she and her family would be killed if she told anything. Medical records disclosed scars on her body and old laboratory reports suggesting a correlation between what she was reporting and her experiences. The local police confirmed that a group which practiced organized abuse of this type was in operation during the time when Ms. T. lived in the same area. A number of other people victimized by the group came forward and told similar stories. (They were living in different areas when the independent reporting started.)

Ms. T. had received several trials of treatment for presumed schizophrenia, which, after a period of sedation, made her worse. Because of new evidence consultants recommended a revision in diagnosis and a different treatment approach. Her therapist of fifteen years disagreed with the new approach. Her psychiatrist stated that since her favorite mentor did not believe that cults exist, neither did she. Her family stated that they would never have allowed her to be placed in a place where such things could happen, and that she would have told them at the time if they did happen. Her direct care staff, who had worked with her since the abuse took place, were insulted that anyone would suggest such things could go on without their knowledge.

(Though the information was extremely clear and increasingly explicitly documented, the reactions of various other providers appeared to delay this woman's treatment for three years.)

Recognition of diagnostic criteria in people who do not speak does not differ significantly from recognition in people who do speak. An intermediate step is that the diagnostician must either learn the person's nonverbal language or use an interpreter who already knows how the person communicates. Equally important is the diagnostician's careful and thorough review of background materials. Sometimes it is easier to document the presence of hypervigilance, nightmares, and other observable symptoms in persons who cannot speak than in others, because of the large number of people involved in observing. The person's behavior as he/she behaves as if re-experiencing the trauma can be explicitly documented. These symptoms may be mislabeled as psychosis—e.g. the person seems to be fighting or hiding from people who aren't there, then a historical review discloses that this is identical to previous experiences. Careful observation and work in developing historic information make it possible to detect and understand symptoms, even in a person who does not use spoken communication (Ryan, 1994). A person may be misdiagnosed as "autistic" because of withdrawal, anxiety, and startle when touched. Of course trauma does not cause autism, and if the "autistic-like" symptoms begin after trauma, and are accompanied by nightmares, phobias, hypervigilance (rather than disinterest), the affected individual likely has P.T.S.D., not autism. Many fear-related symptoms can collected pejorative labels. As an example, an individual who avoids certain situations or settings may be labelled "noncompliant with programming." A person who does not expect to have a future may be thought to be uninterested in the treatment planning process. Since changes caused by unresolved trauma can be quite pervasive, some people are labeled as character disordered. Presence of untreated Axis I or Axis III conditions can stress the person to the extent that he/she appears to have a character disorder, which is an Axis II condition, but treatments of character disorder differ from treatment of P.T.S.D. (and most other Axis I or III conditions), so accurate longitudinal history and symptom description is critical.

A treatment protocol with some database support (Ryan, 1994) includes careful use of medications, complete medical evaluation, appropriate psychotherapy, reduction of iatrogenic factors, habilitative changes to minimize dissociative triggers, and staff training and support.

Several neurotransmitter systems appear to be affected by trauma (Charney, et al., 1993; Goldfeld, et al., 1988; Ito et al., 1993; Jorge, et al., 1993; Teicher, et al., 1993). Careful medication use involves both treatment of comorbid psychiatric conditions and treatment to attenuate the most disabling P.T.S.D. symptoms. The noradrenergic system regulates the "fight or flight" response, and may be distorted to the point where the person is numbed, and/or has an exaggerated "fight or flight" response to any minor reminder of trauma or present danger. Numbing is common in people who have been institutionalized. The exaggerated response is more common in survivors of intensive combat situations, making beta blockers a popular treatment for this population. Unfortunately beta blockers tend to worsen the most common symptoms of P.T.S.D. in people with developmental disabilities—numbing, nightmares, withdrawal, and depression—suggesting that this group of drugs may not be as useful in this population.

The serotonin system, influencing mood and suicidality, is very commonly distorted by chronic trauma, particularly where there is associated a quality of hopelessness and inability to escape. Mood disorders, especially depression, are commonly seen, and should be adequately treated with antidepressants with the least side effects, usually selective serotonin reuptake inhibitors (S.S.R.I.'s). The limbic system serves to integrate an individual's emotional and memory response to stimulation of various sorts. Development of this system can be markedly distorted by chronic trauma that starts early in life. A mood stabilizer, especially anticonvulsants such as carbamazepine or valproic acid, may be especially useful when mood lability or dissociation is prominent.

The dopaminergic system influences a person's sense of reality, and distortion of this system can contribute to intensity of flashbacks. However, medications which act on the dopaminergic system, such as neuroleptics, do not improve dopaminergic transmission directly, but serve to diminish the influence of outside stimuli. This property may be helpful for people with schizophrenia, who have difficulties with filtering stimuli. However, in people with P.T.S.D. without schizophrenia, long term use of antipsychotic medications can make their condition worse, by preventing perception of orienting stimuli needed for healing.

The beta endorphin system is the body's narcotic response to pain. Most people experience some relief of pain when endorphins are released, but do not become addicted to these substances. However, in people with a genetic heritage of altered endorphin perception/use (usually manifesting in alcoholism or narcotics addiction), an addiction to their own endorphins may develop. This can become manifest as chronic scheduled self-mutilation or trauma related alcoholism. Self-mutilation may occur commonly for other reasons in mood disorders and P.T.S.D., so a specific diagnosis of "endogenous opiate addiction " may be complicated. Naltrexone, which blocks the action of narcotics, combined with a 12-step approach, may be useful for people with this particular complication.

The hypothalamic-pituitary axis influences the body's growth and sexual maturity. Although specific treatment is not usually prescribed, delayed or precocious puberty may occur related to trauma. If P.T.S.D. is treated properly, puberty may finally occur.

Complete medical evaluation is essential. The frequency of medical conditions which may influence mental health is, in persons with developmental disabilities and mental health needs, double that seen in persons without developmental disabilities (King, DeAntonio, McCracken, Forness, & Ackerland, 1994; Ryan & Sunada, 1992). Thorough evaluation requires complete physical examination, history taking, and usually more comprehensive laboratory testing than required for people without developmental disabilities (Ryan, 1995).

Appropriate psychotherapy provides the individual an opportunity to be believed, to work through previous trauma, to abstract if necessary, to grieve for lost time and relationships, and to "practice" the "new self." The presence or absence of spoken communication appears irrelevant with regard to treatment or prognosis. The most commonly omitted steps, which delay or derail treatment, are failure of the therapist to develop a respectful alliance and failure of the therapist to use language that is comfortable for the client. These errors often seem to translate to therapists thinking they are supposed to "make the person act nicer" and by wasting a lot of time trying to make the individual communicate in the therapist's most comfortable language. An effective therapist may or may not describe himself/herself as a "D.D. expert." Required characteristics are an understanding of the myriad manifestations of trauma, and creative and eclectic (rather than a single method) approach, and an orientation toward healing rather than control. Most effective therapists work in collaboration with the person's team, assisting the team to become a healing force without becoming overly psychologized. Final stages of treatment allow the person to practice the "new self" free of the fear and constant influence of trauma/loss. Many aspects of psychotherapy are described regularly in the N.A.D.D. Newsletter and Habilitative Mental Healthcare Newsletter. Frequent contributors to information on these matters are Dorothy Griffiths, David Hingsburger, Johnny Matson, Steven Reiss, Pamela Rodden, Dick Sobsey, Christine Stavrakaki, and numerous others.

Reduction of iatrogenic factors may involve changes in environment, medications, contacts, and personnel. A healing environment allows for only a reasonable noise level (less in persons who may have hypersensitive hearing), privacy, safety, and comfort. Large congregate settings rarely meet these criteria, though even in these settings well-motivated providers can see that these things do occur. Often the first obstacle to overcome is the idea that people are required to take what is available, often because of "expense," although many studies show that individualizing settings actually saves money. Medications which have negative psychiatric side effects may interfere with healing. Hundreds of medications may have this possible effect (The Medical Letter, 1989), but the most common offenders are H_2 blockers, phenytoin, barbiturate anticonvulsants, diuretics, and beta blockers. If any of these medications are being prescribed, they probably should be discontinued and more benign alternatives used. Unnecessary sedation is another form of medication iatrogenesis. This may interfere with person's participation in other parts of healing. Additionally, in many settings people who were traumatized and subsequently became agitated were "put to sleep" with sedative antipsychotic medication. In this way the effect of medication could come to be associated with trauma, eventually making the medication a trigger of dissociation or flashbacks. The individual should not be required to work or play with people who frighten them, who remind them of abusers, or who have been abusers, whether staff, colleagues, community personnel, or family members. Unfortunately, on occasion, in an effort to preserve the family, survivors of abuse have been forced to have continuing contact with previously abusive and unrepentant family members.

Illustrative Case #2: M. R., a 6-year old boy who does not use spoken communication, was placed in foster care at three years of age because of severe neglect and abuse. Many different types of abuse had been perpetrated by the mother and several stepfather. The most carefully documented were three attempts by the mother to kill M. R.. These attempts included attempted drowning, beating on the head, and throwing him out of a moving vehicle. He survived all of these attempts.

His current foster care provider was not told any of this information because of "confidentiality concerns." When the biologic mother appeared and stated she wanted to try to reinitiate a relationship with M.R., the foster care provider felt obligated to assist. The mother showed some anxiety associated with the visits, which she explained as being due to the extreme nature of M.R.'s "behaviors" in the past. Apparently he had broken several large and expensive items of furniture when he was very small. After visits with his mother M.R. was hyperactive, incontinent of urine and feces, woke up screaming four or five times per night, hid under his bed, and hit or kicked everyone who worked with him. This behavior was felt to be his expression of unhappiness that the visits were over. His behavior also escalated just prior to visits.

At a hearing regarding termination of parental rights the judge ruled that, when acts perpetrated by the mother continued to haunt the child, his rights to feel safe superseded her rights to have her acts kept secret. The judge further emphasized that no act of this child could be considered extreme in the face of responding to attempted murder by his mother, and his efforts of vigorous protest were respected as such, rather than characterized as oppositional acts of a "bad kid." When appropriate information was shared, M.R.'s team attempted a trial of no visits with the mother. During this trial he made developmental gains, and his self-injury, aggression, and incontinence improved. When he began to talk he said "Don't let her near me."

A team which facilitates contact with an abuser exposes the individual to fear and danger. Also, the person's trust in the system and staff, which would allow this to go on, is undermined. On occasion there is confusion when the person seems to be asking to have contact with an abuser, which may actually be a request for assurance that the team will definitely not allow the contact. At other times the person may be expressing the wish that someone nonabusive would assume the previous role of the abuser. A way to check this is to ask the individual what they want to do when the see the abuser. Another possibility is the rare instance where an abuser has accepted responsibility for their actions, is working furiously to make amends, apologizes continuously both in works and actions, and seeks advice and supervision of others. IF this is the case, and IF the individual seems to genuinely desire contact, there may be some possibility of allowing contact.

Another problem situation is the case in which there is a suspicion that someone is being abused, but no evidence. In this instance it is important to facilitate the person sharing what they can, but it is absolutely critical that the individual not be led. Disapproval of any abuse of the person should be very explicit, and a desire to protect if needed should be communicated. Orientation toward assistance with security and safety is often useful, and power struggles should be avoided.

Habilitative changes include analysis of the environment for triggers of dissociation, reduction of or desensitization to those triggers, and healing interventions during flashbacks. Triggers of flashbacks may include any sort of stimulation, anniversaries, death of an abuser, contact with an abuser, other unrelated stresses/losses, or when a person's children reach an age when the abuse occurred. Aromas are often a very powerful trigger. As an example, a person may have flashbacks when smelling the cologne of an abuser. Sometimes knowing that something is or has been a trigger can be enough to reduce its impact. "I saw how little my baby was when he was three, it made me see how small I was when she burned me. I'm big now, I won't let it happen to my baby or to me no more." Other times it is necessary to remove a trigger. One man had flashbacks when a staff member posted nude pictures of his own children that happened to be age the individual was when he was abused. The pictures were removed, with a cessation of the flashbacks. Some people choose to be desensitized to triggers. For example, one man experienced flashbacks whenever a train went by his home. He did not want to leave his home, so strategies were developed to cope and deflect flashbacks. During flashbacks staff are trained to be supportive and reorienting, with supportive nonpersonal contact, confident assurances about where and when the person is, and assurances that nothing will be allowed to happen to the person. "Jane, it's 1995, it feels like XXX is here, but he isn't, it's Ruth, and we won't let anyone hurt you. Tell me where you are." (All of this is stated while remaining calm and hold the person's hands or shoulders in a supportive, nonthreatening manner.) Anger, fear, restraints, and reprimands are contraindicated.

Staff training and support are focused on arming the team with all information necessary for understanding symptoms in context, so they can act as healers. Without this information staff members may be inadvertently forced into the position of perpetrators. At the very least uninformed staff tend to become fearful, controlling, and blaming, because they only see very intense symptoms, without any context. Implementation of controlling or punitive procedures may frighten the person into temporary compliance, but these procedures eventually lead to deterioration, which can also "burn out" staff. Ongoing training and support meetings of staff members are useful. The tasks of these meetings include sharing of new didactic information, sharing of serendipitous programming findings, celebrating progress, and early intervention in problems. Common problems include staff members that split off from the rest of the team in an effort to be heroes, staff members that start to deal with their own trauma issues in ways that are nonproductive, and staff members that resonate in a nonhelpful way with the individual's fear, helplessness, or anger. Usually well-informed staff members take ideas and preliminary techniques and improve on them, tailoring them to the specific individual. Developing written and videotape records of successful interventions may be extremely important for documentation and training, especially in times of limited resources and rapid turnover.

If there were no abusers and no trauma in the world there would be no posttraumatic stress disorder. Abuse prevention is presently being studied by Dr. Dorothy Griffiths and associates at Brock University in Ontario. Prevention of other traumas of life such as horrible deaths of loved ones, fires, and natural disasters probably cannot be carried out.

Secondary prevention practices as the reactions of team members when trauma occurs may assist in preventing or minimizing many of the long term sequelae. Standard protocols for assisting people who have experienced specific types of trauma, such as rape, combat exposure, or hurricanes, have been developed, but since people are not alike, these are not always successful. Major principles involve being present and respectful, and always trying to find out what each specific person would find empowering, while still making certain that a reliable individual is able to keep contact with the affected person to check on safety and progress. Another key principle is respect for whatever emotional reaction the person emits. Screaming, crying, twisted humor, howling, or intense irritability may all be appropriate. Making certain the person tells the entire story, in whatever way they communicate, to someone safe as soon as possible is important. It is also important the person be able to share this information with trusted people whenever they feel the need. Some individuals may need some other nonspecific comfort procedures for an interval, and this need should be respected. Examples of this sort of activity might include overeating, excessive exercise, overwork, vacation from work, cleaning out all the closets, or watching favorite movies continuously and repetitively. Whatever the person uses to soothe and empower themselves should be respected.

Procedures guaranteed to worsen the impact of trauma include blaming the person for the trauma ("well,if you would get home you were supposed to you wouldn't get raped"), making fun of the person's increased need for security ("wearing those extra clothes to bed now is silly"),or forcing the person to have contact with someone they don't want to see right at the time ("every girl needs her mother at a time like this"). One woman who was raped in her group home stated she absolutely did not want to see her father, and wanted to see her older sister only. The team insisted it knew better, stating she should definitely have her father there, especially since he was a physician. Against his better judgement, because he thought the team ought to know, after all,he came in and participated in restraining her while the rape exam was conducted. To this day she believes it was her father who raped her, and has nightmares to that effect, even though her father was out of the country when the rape occurred. "Pretend like nothing happened" is another piece of poor advice that was popular years ago, and definitely makes the situation worse. Some people still suggest that if everyone just pretends as if everything is alright the person will just "cover over" and forget. Persons with developmental disabilities have already had decades of experience of people ignoring their experiences of trauma and pretending as if they do not have mental health needs. If it was going to help, it would have helped by now. We can do better.

In summary, P.T.S.D. is an anxiety disorder that is one of several possible sequelae of serious trauma. Accurate and careful diagnosis allows for specific and effective treatment. Whether or not a person uses spoken communication is irrelevant with regard to diagnosis, treatment, or prognosis. Ignoring is not helpful. Prevention may be possible with updated approaches to intervention.

References

American Psychiatric Association. (1994). *Diagnostic and statistical manual of mental disorders, 4th edition*. Washington, DC: author.

Blatt, B. (1970). *Exodus from Pandemonium*. Boston: Allyn and Bacon.

Blatt, B. & Kaplan, F. (1966). *Christmas in Purgatory*. Boston: Allyn and Bacon.

Charney, D. S., Deutsch, A. Y., Krystal, J. H., Southwick, S. M., & Davis, M. (1993). Psychobiological mechanisms of posttraumatic stress disorder, *Archives of General Psychiatry, 50*: 294-305.

Drugs which cause psychiatric symptoms. (1989). *Medical Letter Drug Therapy, 31*: 113-118.

Goldfeld, A. E., Mollica, R. F., Pesavento, B. H., & Faraone, S. V. (1988). The physical and psychological sequelae of torture, *Journal of the American Medical Association, 259*: 2725-2729.

Ito, Y., Teicher, M. H., Glod, C. A., Harper, D., Magnus, E., & Gelbard, H. A. (1993). Increased prevalence of electrophysiologic abnormalities in children with physiologic, physical, and sexual abuse, *Journal of Neuropsychiatry and Clinical Neuroscience, 5*: 401-408.

Jorge, R. E., Robinson, R. G., Starkstein, S. E., & Arndt, S. V. (1993). Depression and anxiety following traumatic brain injury, *Journal of Neuropsychiatry and Clinical Neuroscience, 5*:369-374.

King, B. H., DeAntonio, C., McCracken, J. T., Forness, S. R., & Ackerland, V. (1994). Psychiatric consultation in severe and profound mental retardation, *American Journal of Psychiatry, 151*:1802-1808.

Ryan, R. M. (in press). Neuropsychiatry and persons with developmental disabilities. In F. Ovsiew (Ed.), *Neuropsychiatry in the Community*. Washington, DC: American Psychiatric Press.

Ryan, R. M. (1995). Posttraumatic stress disorder in persons with developmental disabilities, *Community Mental Health Journal, 30*:45-54.

Ryan, R. M. (1994). Recognition of psychosis in persons that do not use spoken communication. In R. J. Ancill, S. Holliday, & J. Higgenbottam (Eds.), *Schizophrenia: Exploring the Spectrum of Psychosis*. New York: Wiley and Sons.

Ryan, R. M. & Sunada, K. (1992). Medical assessment of persons with developmental disabilities and mental health needs. Presentation at N.A.D.D. annual meeting.

Sobsey, D. (1994). *Violence and Abuse in the Lives of People With Developmental Disabilities: The End of Silent Acceptance?*. Baltimore, MD: Brookes Publishing.

Teicher, M. H., Glod, C. A., Surrey, J., & Swett, C. (1993). Early childhood abuse and limbic system ratings in adult psychiatric outpatients, *Journal of Neuropsychiatry and Clinical Neuroscience, 5*:301-306.

U.S. Commission on Civil Rights. (September, 1989). *Medical discrimination against children with disabilities*. Washington, DC: author.

NONPHARMACOLOGIC TREATMENT OF ANXIETY DISORDERS: ONE WOMAN'S STORY

CATHERINE A. SALIGA, L.C.S.W.

LARK KIRCHNER, R.N., L.C.S.W.

E. L. LOSCHEN, M.D.

**Southern Illinois University School of Medicine
Department of Psychiatry**

Anxiety is the most common mental health problem in the United States (Danton, Altrocchi, & Basta, 1994). Individuals with mental retardation would be expected to be vulnerable to anxiety disorders also, and not be an exception, since they are vulnerable to the full range of psychiatric disorders (Reiss, 1994). Unfortunately, anxiety disorders have been among the least of those studied in individuals who have mental retardation. It is not clear "whether the relative paucity of data is due to diagnostic overshadowing and related biases or to a genuinely low prevalence of these syndromes" (McNally, 1991) within individuals with mental retardation. Other noted investigators, Hurley, Sovner, Jackson, Ollendick, and Ollendick, have also commented on the lack of studies, as noted by McNally in 1991. Because of this several questions arise. Is the diagnosis of anxiety being completely missed in this population, or at best under-recognized? Are individuals with mental retardation receiving the same treatments for anxiety as are received by non-cognitively impaired individuals? Since individuals with mental retardation have problems with coping effectively in stressful situations, and stressful situations may be common for these individuals, these may be contributing factors in anxiety, which may lead to a mental disorder (Chiodo & Maddux, 1985; Dosen, 1993).

Some reports indicate that anxiety-based problems are more common in people with mental retardation than in those without mental retardation (McNally, 1991). If this is the case, then treatments that are available to the general population should be made available to individuals with a dual diagnosis (mental retardation and mental health conditions) unless systematic assessment indicates a contraindication. It is our responsibility to study, research, and advocate for a full range of mental health services, including nonpharmacologic treatments, to be available to the individuals we serve. Further, there is a need to adequately address the prevalence of the various anxiety disorders and the efficacy of treatment given for specific disorders. Literature reviews indicate that, though disorders of anxiety are understudied, a considerable amount of writing exists relating to symptoms or presentations of anxiety symptoms in this population. T.H. Ollendick and Ollendick (1982) note that as early as the 1920's Potter documented specific emotional problems of individuals with mental retardation, and noted problems with "nervous energy." They further point out that Tredgold in 1947 referenced anxiety states and obsessive compulsive reactions as occurring frequently with individuals with mental retardation. Certain there has not been a lack of observation about disorders relevant to anxiety, just little study related to prevalence and treatment efficacy.

Our intention in this paper is to demonstrate an assessment and treatment planning process, using a case illustration of an individual who was diagnosed with a generalized anxiety disorder and received nonpharmacological interventions. This case study will provide an overview of our current assessment, diagnostic, and treatment process for individuals who may have an anxiety disorder and mental retardation.

Clinic for Individuals with Developmental Disability and a Psychiatric Disorder

The Southern Illinois University (S.I.U.) School of Medicine Department of Psychiatry in Springfield, Illinois, established a Special Needs Clinic for individuals with a developmental disability who also have a psychiatric or behavioral disorder. This clinic offers psychiatric services that include psychiatric evaluation, service needs assessment, treatment planning, and pharmacological and nonpharmacological interventions.

Interventions used within an outpatient setting include person-centered planning, group and individual psychotherapy, and behavioral interventions. A team approach is used to provide a comprehensive treatment planning process. The team consists of psychiatrists, social workers, and a behavioral specialist.

Evaluation Protocol

Evaluation protocols have been developed in the outpatient service in order to ensure accuracy in diagnostic formulations, appropriate treatment planning, and to provide a data base for study of treatment outcomes. During intake and when particular problems present a specific evaluation protocol is followed. (See Tables 1 and 2.) The individual's presenting problems determine the specific assessments used. During the course of treatment planning other assessments may be used to measure outcomes.

Table 1

Assessment Items to Use With All Presenting Problems at Intake

    Mental Health Assessment (& consent to assess)

    Releases

    Social History

    Current physical (6 months)

    S.I.U. Medication History

    Behavioral Analysis S.I.U. form

    Labs

        CBC

        Chem 20

    Adaptive Behavior Evaluation (I.C.A.P., S.I.B.,A.A.M.R.)

    Psychological (W.A.I.S.-R., Stanford Binet)

    A.I.M.S.

    T.E.S.S.

    D.A.S.H. (severe/prof.levels; adults/adolescents)

    P.I.M.R.A. (self report & others; mild-moderate;

    adults/adolescents)

    REISS (all ages/all levels

Table 2
Assessment Items to Use With Specified Presenting Problems at
Intake or at the Time of Diagnosis of Individual Symptoms
Presenting Problems:
    S.I.B.
        A.B.C. (Ages 5-adult; mild-profound M.R.)
        Akathisia Scale
        B.P.I. (children and adults of all levels)
        M.A.S. (all levels; frequency >15/hour)
        S.I.B.Q.
    Physical Aggression
        A.B.C.
        Akathisia Scale
        B.P.I.
        M.A.S.
    Anxiety
        Akathisia Scale
        ZUNG Anxiety Scale Modified (mild/mod.,
        adults)
    Depression Symptoms
        A.B.C.
        ZUNG Depression Scale Modified (mild/mod.,
        adolescents/adults)
    Medication Evaluation
        A.B.C.
        Akathisia Scale
    Other
        p.r.n.
    Psychosis
        A.B.C.
        Akathisia Scale

**Case Illustration: Assessment as the Initial Step
to Effective Treatment**

    A young woman was referred to the Special Needs Clinic for a psychiatric evaluation. Facts presented at the initial evaluation included age, basic identifying information, a psychological evaluation with the level of mental retardation, and the diagnosis of cerebral palsy. Basic social history information included history of residential living and educational history. Presenting symptoms included fatigue, loss of energy, feelings of worthlessness, middle insomnia, decreased ability to concentrate at work, increased appetite, and frequent crying. Care providers and the individual herself explained that she was a recent victim of domestic violence, had moved, and had started a new job. All of these events had occurred within a short period of time. At the time of initial evaluation the current protocols were not yet in place, and the diagnostic formulation was based on the presenting facts and psychiatric evaluation. Major stressors identified included the move, new job, and domestic violence. Diagnosis given at that time was an Axis I diagnosis of Adjustment Disorder with Depressed Mood, and individual therapy was recommended. A psychodynamic approach to therapy was taken, to resolve the adjustment issues and to attempt to assist the individual to gain some insight into her situation. A cognitive approach was incorporated to assist the individual to gain problems solving skills and develop coping strategies. After twelve individual sessions most of her adjustment issues were resolved, and the more debilitating symptoms were alleviated. As a result, individual therapy was terminated based on mutual agreement between the individual and the therapist. The team, including the individual, decided that, since she continued to identify interpersonal relationship issues, she would be transferred into group therapy. Of note was the fact that she believed that group therapy was a graduation from individual therapy, and she repeatedly verbalized her positive feelings about being able to be in a group.

Subsequent to the development of evaluation protocols, specific cases were revisited. The evaluation protocols have underscored the importance of systematic and data-based assessment in establishing diagnosis, treatment planning, and outcome evaluation. This specific case was revisited because the individual identified further problems that affected her overall day-to-day functioning. An anecdotal observation of the use of group therapy has been the ability to provide assessment of problems that often are not evident in the initial psychiatric evaluation, and also allows an opportunity for the person to relate significant life events in a comfortable and supportive environment.

This case illustration provides a framework for demonstration of the relevant elements of the assessment phase, which include obtaining a social history that incorporated a developmental history and a resume of significant life events, an analysis of psychotherapy sessions including the therapist's observations of the individual's coping strategies, defining and recording of symptom response, reports from caregivers, clinical interview, and standardized assessment tools. These elements were considered valuable pieces of the diagnostic puzzle, and resulted in a more comprehensive assessment that defined treatment strategies. These elements are specifically addressed and described in more detail throughout this paper.

Collecting an extensive history provides the clinician with information on the occurrence of significant life events as well as a means to evaluate the efficacy of the individual's coping strategies. A social history should include childhood development factors, family history and significant family events, residential history, specific reasons for moving, and educational and vocational history. Some of the significant events that were identified in this case and considered serious stressors included early childhood physical abuse, subsequent physical abuse by male residential peers and male significant others, alleged sexual abuse, numerous eye and orthopedic leg surgeries during childhood, parents divorced, mother remarried, two siblings, graduation from special education, moving to a home for individuals with disabilities during late adolescence, being hired and fired from jobs, and multiple moves.

An in-depth review of past evaluations provided useful diagnostic information. In this case a past psychological evaluation was reviewed which identified impressions and recommendations that had never been implemented. A previously administered adaptive behavior scale described the person as bossy and manipulative, disruptive of others, and a loud talker, who demanded excess attention and did not pay attention. During this psychological assessment concerns about a move, concerns about a grandmother, and recent deaths were identified as relevant affective issues. The psychologist's treatment recommendation was counseling for anxiety!

In this case the review of documentation from psychotherapy sessions proved to be beneficial, particularly the outcomes and associated symptoms. This review may identify underlying problems, themes, stressors, and coping strategies or lack thereof. In this specific case issues and problems addressed in her past sessions of individual psychotherapy included physical and sexual abuse, relationship issues, middle insomnia, excessive talking, heart pounding, irritability, poor concentration, "hot" feelings, and poor appetite. At the conclusion of individual psychotherapy positive outcomes had been achieved, including improvement in sleep pattern and appetite, increased concentration at work, positive feelings about coworkers and family, some insight about the situation, and the desire to move forward. Additional skills attained in therapy were recognition of physical symptoms of distress and ability to call and report these symptoms during periods of emotional distress. One issue still persisted— she continued to repeatedly list her problems and worries.

The importance of reports from caregivers should never be overlooked or under-emphasized. The people who known an individual best can always provide the most critical information. Caregivers can help the clinician to prioritize, explain the severity, and investigate the functions of the presented problems. This will enable the clinician to understand how the individual's life is being affected and what treatment might be most beneficial. The caregiver's perspective or interpretation of the problem may also be a contributing factor to the individual's problem. However, this is a life situation with which many people with disabilities must cope, so there is a need to evaluate the individual's relationships and their skill of interacting with their paid caregivers.

The summary of information in this case, collected from the social history, review of past psychotherapy notes, reports from caregivers, and formalized assessment tools, pointed in the direction of anxiety as a diagnostic consideration. The evaluation protocol was followed and assessments identified for anxiety problems were selected and completed. Assessments selected were Reiss Screen for Maladaptive Behavior, Zung Self Rating Anxiety Scale, and Psychopathology Inventory for Mentally Retarded Adults (P.I.M.R.A.).

A clinical interview provides the setting for gathering information from both the individual and caregivers. Goals that are critical for accurate assessment are establishing a positive relationship between the client and clinician, obtaining specific information regarding target behaviors, observation of the client's reactions to the interview setting, and determination of the presence of generalized anxiet. Standardized assessments can be used and completed in this setting.

The Zung Self-Rating Anxiety Scale was identified as an assessment tool for anxiety disorders in individuals with mild to moderate mental retardation in the evaluation protocol. The P.I.M.R.A. has a subscale of anxiety in both the self-report version and the report by others. Both of these assessments are used in the Special Needs Clinic to identify and measure anxiety symptoms in individuals with mild to moderate mental retardation. The Hamilton Anxiety Scale, Zung (not modified), and the Beck's Anxiety Scale were also used in this case.

After completion of this assessment we felt this individual has an Axis I diagnosis of Generalized Anxiety Disorder. She demonstrated specific anxiety behavioral presentations and physical cues, including excessive worrying, irritability, inability to stay focused, decline in hygiene skills, inability to collect and organize information, fatigue, sleep disturbance, clammy hands, racing heart, headaches, dry mouth, body tension, hot flashes and "pins and needles" feelings. Standardized assessment instruments identified by the evaluation protocol and by the clinician for specific use with this individual had positive results for anxiety. The Reiss Screen for Maladaptive Behavior was positive for dual diagnosis. The P.I.M.R.A. identified Anxiety and Personality disorders as diagnostic consideration, while the Hamilton and Zung scores ranked her anxiety as mild to moderate degree of severity.

Case Illustration: Treatment Strategies

This case illustrates the importance of treatment planning as a process. A process is a series of events, and treatment planning does not occur just initially or at prescribed intervals, but rather when symptomatology dictates a change in strategy or further reassessment defines a need for treatment revision. Development of a diagnostic impression upon which to base treatment strategies was the first step. The second step involved revisitation of the case and application of refined protocols as the individual presented with new or reappearance of symptoms. The process had an empowering effect for this individual and the treatment plan. She was able to identify and direct the course of the treatment.

Many nonpharmacologic strategies have been proven effective in treating anxiety in the general population. Some of these effective strategies that should be considered for individuals with mental retardation who have an anxiety disorder include anxiety management, social skills training, behavioral biofeedback, differential reinforcement of other behavior, modeling, lifestyle accommodations, education and support for staff, environmental manipulation, performance feedback, psychotherapy, cognitive behavioral therapy, relaxation training, in vivo exposure, and imaginal exposure. McNally's (1991) review of anxiety disorders describes the various anxiety diagnoses and treatments with known studies of efficacy. McNally and Ascher (1987) reviewed treatment approaches for people who have both mental retardation and anxiety disorders. Evidence reviewed suggested that techniques such as relaxation, exposure in vivo, and social skills training require little modification to be effective with people with mental retardation.

A treatment plan for this individual was formulated which included both individual and group psychotherapy. Cognitive and behavioral approaches would be the focus, in order to use specific strategies such as relaxation, anxiety management, problem-solving techniques, crisis management, and social skills training. This approach and these interventions were chosen to involve the individual as an active participant in learning to further identify and manage her anxiety. Self-assessment skills were taught to identify the times she is in a state of anxiety. Relaxation training was used as a counter-conditioning technique to help reduce the anxiety symptoms. Studies have shown that progressive relaxation training has been effective in treating many mental health conditions, including anxiety, behavioral, and cognitive difficulties (Lindsay, Baty, Michie, & Richardson, 1989; Rickard, Thrasher, & Elkins, 1984; Harvey, 1979). Progressive relaxation involves the tension and relaxation of muscle groups followed by cognitive focusing on physiological relaxation (Rickard, et al., 1993). This type of relaxation training was the instructional method used.

Case Illustration: Outcomes

After the completion of six sessions, individual therapy was terminated, once again by mutual agreement of the individual and the therapist. The individual identified positive outcomes as the acquisition of anxiety and anger management skills, body awareness, relaxation skills, ability to express feelings, and improved work skills. Specific personal anxiety management techniques were taught, to promote generalization from the individual therapy sessions to real life situations. The ability to provide the individual with educational and long-term means to deal with stressful situations is an important issue which should be addressed and be a component of the treatment plan (Chiodo & Maddux, 1985). Techniques that this individual found helpful included self-assessment skills, role playing, journal keeping, fact collection, job checklists, and problem solving. Also, a relaxation video tape was made from one of her sessions, to encourage her to practice at home and to use relaxation as a coping strategy in her everyday life. She continues to participate in weekly group therapy sessions, and has recently volunteered to teach relaxation techniques to the group.

Discussion

The case illustration just described certainly underscores the fact that occurrence of anxiety disorder is possible in some individuals with mental retardation. Our data show that our clinic continues to under-diagnose anxiety, and than numerous cases are being revisited as a result of the protocol. This case illustration indicates the need for systematic assessment and reassessment. Studies show that development of an assessment which allows individuals with I.Q.s below 60 to understand and describe feelings of anxiety is very difficult (Reiss, 1994; Lindsay & Michie, 1988). However, assessment tools are available and those assessment tools used for noncognitively impaired individuals should not be overlooked, especially with individuals who are in the mild range of mental retardation and are able to report their symptoms. These specific tools may be used in conjunction with instruments that have been adapted for this population and with clinical observation.

The importance of data collection and reliable social history gathering is clear in cases involving anxiety, and certainly most notably with abuse histories. The effect of repeated moves and program changes made during significant life events may also give necessary information for the consideration of psychotherapy. In this particular case the use of collaborative teamwork allowed us to focus on the individual's symptomatology in organized fashion, and allowed us to use a nonpharmacological approach that continues to be positive for the individual. We intend to have this case guide us to further studies with individuals whose assessment and life events suggest the presence of an anxiety disorder.

References

Chiodo, J. & Maddux, J. E. (1985). A cognitive and behavioral approach to anxiety management of retarded individuals: Two case studies. *Journal of Child and Adolescent Psychotherapy, 2*, 16-20.

Danton, W. G., Altrocchi, A. D., & Basta, R. (1994). Nondrug treatment of anxiety. *American Family Physician, 49*, 161-166.

Dosen, A. (1993). Mental health and mental illness in persons with retardation: What are we talking about?. In R. J. Fletcher & A. Dosen (Eds.), *Mental health aspects of mental retardation: Progress in assessment and treatment* (pp.3-17). New York: Lexington Books.

Harvey, J. R. (1979). The potential of relaxation training for the mentally retarded. *Mental Retardation, 17,* 71-76.

Lindsay, W. R., Baty, F. J., Michie, A. M., & Richardson, I. (1989). A comparison of anxiety treatments with adults who have moderate and severe mental retardation. *Research in Developmental Disabilities, 10,* 129-140.

Lindsay, W. R. & Michie, A. M. (1988). Adaptation of the Zung self-rating anxiety scale for people with a mental handicap. *Journal of Mental Deficiency Research, 32,* 485-490.

McNally, R. J. (1991). Anxiety and phobias. In J. L. Matson & J. A. Mulick (Eds.), *Handbook of mental retardation* (pp.413-423). New York: Pergamon Press.

McNally, R. J. & Ascher, L. M. (1987). Anxiety disorders in mentally retarded people. In L. Michelson & L. M. Ascher (Eds.), *Anxiety and stress disorders: Cognitive-behavioral assessment and treatment.* New York: Guilford Press.

Ollendick, T. H. & Ollendick, D. G. (1982). Anxiety disorders. In J. L. Matson & R. P. Barrett (Eds.), *Psychopathology in the mentally retarded* (pp.77-119). New York: Grune & Stratton.

Reiss, S. (1994). *Handbook of challenging behaviors: Mental health aspects of mental retardation.* Worthington, OH: IDS Publishing.

Rickard, H. C., Collier, J. B., McCoy, A. D., Crist, D. A., & Weinberger, M. B. (1993). Relaxation training for psychiatric inpatients. *Psychological Reports, 72,* 1267-1274.

Rickard, H. C., Thrasher, K. A., & Elkins, P.D. (1984). Responses of persons who are mentally retarded to four components of relaxation instruction. *Mental Retardation, 22,* 248-252.

THE CONCEPT OF ANXIETY SENSITIVITY: POSSIBLE IMPLICATIONS FOR RESEARCH ON DUAL DIAGNOSIS

STEVEN REISS, PH.D.

Ohio State University

Anxiety sensitivity refers to individual differences in what people think will happen to them when they experience anxiety (Reiss, et al., 1986). Some individuals believe that anxiety has catastrophic consequences; for example, these people worry that anxiety leads to panic attacks, mental illness, or heart attacks. Other individuals believe that anxiety is an unpleasant but otherwise harmless experience. The more anxiety sensitivity beliefs a person has, and the more strongly each belief is held, the higher the level of anxiety sensitivity. People who believe that anxiety has catastrophic personal consequences are said to have high anxiety sensitivity, whereas people who believe that anxiety is an unpleasant but harmless experience are said to have low anxiety sensitivity.

Anxiety sensitivity is measured by a brief, 16-item self-report instrument called the Reiss-Epstein-Gursky Anxiety Sensitivity Index (A.S.I.). In the last decade more than sixty validity studies have been published documenting the psychometric properties of the A.S.I. and providing evidence of concurrent, construct, and predictive validity. Panic Disorder and Post-Traumatic Stress Disorder are associated with A.S.I. scores about two standard deviations above average, whereas other anxiety disorders are associated with scores about one standard deviation above average. Some people with alcoholism and other types of substance abuse also show elevated A.S.I. scores. In laboratory situations anxiety sensitivity has been found to be a risk factor for panic reactions to biological challenges (McNally, 1994).

When the concept of anxiety sensitivity was first introduced, it contradicted a number of widely-held assumptions about panic disorder with agoraphobia. At the time, it was widely assumed that the fear of having a panic attack was a consequence, not a cause, of panic and phobic avoidance. The commonly held idea was that after people experience panic attacks they develop a fear of recurrence, so that the fear of panic and anxiety sensation commonly seen in certain patients with anxiety was simply an expectation that past attacks might recur. In contrast to this view, anxiety sensitivity theory held that catastrophic beliefs about the consequences of anxiety not only could be held prior to any panic attacks but also were a risk factor for panic disorder. That is, one reason some people may panic in the first place is because they misinterpret the bodily and behavioral signs of anxiety/stress as a sign of impending heart attacks, mental illness, and/or other disaster. While the first panic attack may well lead to an expectation of additional attacks, in anxiety sensitivity theory this fear of recurrence is considered an anxiety expectancy that is distinguished from the anxiety sensitivity.

While anxiety sensitivity theory is associated with a number of counterintuitive predictions—many of which have been confirmed (McNally, 1994; Peterson & Reiss, 1992)—perhaps the most interesting suggestion is the possibility of a risk factor for Panic Disorder and other conditions such as substance abuse. One hypothesis is that adolescents with high anxiety sensitivity are at risk to develop a Panic Disorder in adulthood. Theoretically it may be possible to use the A.S.I., which has been translated into nine languages, as an early screen for risk factors for Panic Disorder and related conditions.

Implications for Mental Retardation

The implications of anxiety sensitivity for mental retardation are certainly worth exploring. A Child Anxiety Sensitivity Index (C.A.S.I.) was constructed by adapting A.S.I. items for children . An initial study found that the C.A.S.I. had psychometric properties similar to those for the A.S.I., and that the C.A.S.I. was related to fearfulness in much the same manner as was the A.S.I. (Silverman, et al., 1991).

The extent to which anxiety sensitivity can be measured in people with mild mental retardation needs to be evaluated. The A.S.I. has proven to be an unusually valid psychometric instrument, but with people with mental retardation self-report instruments tend to have low reliability.

In terms of future research two possible implications are discussed here for possible future research. One possible implication concerns the occurrence of various subtypes of anxiety disorders in people with mental retardation. The other implication concerns the possibility of studying other types of sensitivities and their roles in behavior disorders.

Anxiety Disorders and Mental Retardation

Very little research has been reported on the co-occurrence of anxiety disorders and mental retardation. What little data have been reported, however, raise a number of interesting questions concerning overall prevalence rates and possibly widely varying rates for sub-types. First, there is conflicting evidence concerning overall rates of anxiety disorders in people with mental retardation. Some studies and clinic reports suggest that rates may be too low (Eaton & Menolascino, 1982; Jacobson, 1990; Reiss & Trenn, 1984). Other studies suggest rates comparable with that for the general population (Bouras & Drummond, 1992). There is evidence that anxiety and stress, although not anxiety disorder per se, is more common among people with mental retardation (Epstein, Cullinan, & Polloway, 1986).

Secondly, rates may vary significantly for the different subtypes of anxiety disorders, so that some subtypes may be less common among persons with mental retardation and others may be more common or as common as that for the general population. Fears and general anxiety may be more common in persons with mental retardation. Panic Disorder may be less common, as suggested by the absence of any published reports. Rates for Obsessive-Compulsive Disorder and Posttraumatic Stress Disorder are unknown.

Thirdly, if rates for Panic Disorder are low for people with mental retardation, might low levels of anxiety sensitivity be a factor? Could low level of cognitive ability be associated with few anxiety sensitivity beliefs? How do anxiety sensitivity and Panic Disorder vary with I.Q. and various mental retardation levels?

Reinforcement Sensitivities and Behavior Disorder

Anxiety sensitivity may possibly be viewed as a specific example of a more general category of reinforcement sensitivities. In other words, biological or past learning experiences may determine some important individual differences in the effectiveness of the same reinforcement event. A given quantity of reinforcement (food, praise, attention, escape from aversive stimulation, activity) may be much more reinforcing for some people than for others. There may be important individual differences in sensitivities to attention, aversive stimulation, activity levels, etc..

High levels of reinforcement sensitivity may plausibly be related to behavioral problems. Children who have a high sensitivity to attention, for example, may learn aberrant behaviors in order to obtain high amounts of attention from adults. They may be less likely to satiate with regard to attention.

The concept of reinforcement sensitivities focuses research attention on issues in behavior analysis that have received almost no research attention. By definition, conditioning is a form of learning resulting from temporal associations between responses and reinforcement. Consequently, behavior analysts have focused primarily on associative learning and associative remedies in their research on behavior disorders. In contrast, the concept of reinforcement sensitivity is a nonassociative concept. This concept refers to individual differences in the effectiveness of a given quantity of reinforcement, such as the fact that attention may be much more reinforcing to some people than to others. A theory of reinforcement sensitivity would suggest that a better understanding of individual differences in reinforcement preferences and sensitivities may help unlock some of the mysteries of behavior analysis, especially with regard to improving long-term persistence and generalization of behavioral treatment effects.

In conclusion, researchers can study individual differences in reinforcement preferences and sensitivities. Once reliable and valid measures are developed, it would be of interest to relate these measures to outcomes measures regarding the occurrence and treatment of severe behavior disorders. For example, it might be predicted that high rates of reinforcement sensitivity are risk factors for severe behavior problems in people with mental retardation. If this is true, it might lead to early intervention strategies. Theoretically, treatment may need to reduce the high reinforcement sensitivities for the best chance of favorable generalization and persistence.

References

Bouras, N. & Drummond, C. (1992). Behavior and psychiatric disorders of people with mental handicaps living in the community. *Journal of Intellectual Disability Research, 36,* 349-357.

Eaton, L. F. & Menolascino, F. J. (1982). Psychiatric disorders in the mentally retarded: Types, problems, and challenges. *American Journal of Psychiatry, 139,* 1297-1303.

Epstein, M. H., Cullinan, D., & Polloway, E. A. (1986). Patterns of maladjustment among mentally retarded children and youth. *American Journal on Mental Deficiency, 91,* 127-134.

Jacobson, J. W. (1990). Do some mental disorders occur less frequently among persons with mental retardation? *American Journal on Mental Retardation, 94,* 596-602.

McNally, R. J. (1994). *Panic Disorder: A Critical Analysis.* New York: Guilford.

Peterson, R. A. & Reiss, S. (1992). *Anxiety Sensitivity Index revised test manual.* Worthington, OH: IDS Publishing Corporation.

Reiss, S., Peterson, R. A., Gursky, D. M., & McNally, R. J. (1986). Anxiety sensitivity, anxiety frequency, and the prediction of fearfulness. *Behavior Research and Therapy, 24,* 1-8.

Reiss, S. & Trenn, E. (1984). Consumer demand for outpatient mental health services for mentally retarded people. *Mental Retardation, 22,* 112-115.

Silverman, W. I., Flesig, W., Rabian, B., & Peterson, R. A. (1991). Childhood Anxiety Sensitivity Index. *Journal of Clinical Child Psychology, 20,* 162-168.

TEACHING STAFF MEMBERS ABOUT ANXIETY DISORDERS

ANN R. POINDEXTER, M.D.

Since any specific diagnosis of anxiety disorders relies heavily on an individual's ability to describe his/her symptoms, psychiatric symptom history for persons with mental retardation usually must be obtained from multiple informants, ideally from two or more informants who have known the individual well for a period of at least several years (King, et al., 1994). Diagnosis often involves analysis of information from members of the individual's interdisciplinary team, particularly from direct support staff members. Retention of experienced direct support staff is a significant problem in all service programs for persons with mental retardation. While the training curriculum they describe involved communication skills rather than specific technical information, Smoot and Gonzales (1995) found, while evaluating cost-benefits of a staff training program designed to improve patient management skills and relieve staff stress, that the trained unit had less staff turnover and staff members used less sick and annual leave than did the control unit.

Because of the scarcity of "live" training programs on clinical psychiatric issues and the importance of day-to-day staff coverage issues, some type of self-directed instructional system may be of practical importance, particularly in community-based programs. Piskurich in 1993 defined self-directed learning as a training design in which trainees master packages of predetermined material, at their own pace, without the aid of an instructor. He noted that strengths of self-directed learning include availability when the training is needed, not when a class is being held; nonreliance on an instructor, which not only increases availability but decreases cost; on-site implementation, so trainees don't waste time and money traveling; and consistency of presentation, since self-directed learning packages present the same information each time they are used. Piskurich further points out that advantages for trainees include availability when the trainee is ready, trainee works at his/her own pace, individual choice of material, no surprises, immediate feedback, and provision of review and reference. Advantages for the trainer/developer include no constantly repeated classes, less time in travel, and more time for development. Advantages for corporations or other employers include multiple-site training, reduced meeting-room cost, ability to capture knowledge of subject matter experts, fewer trainers required, reduced trainer travel costs, elimination of trainee travel costs, just-in-time training, downtime training, no training classes when busy, easier shift training, possibility of cross-training, training consistency, and less aggregate time spent.

Some trainees, however, are not comfortable with absence of an instructor or relying on objectives. Disadvantages for the trainer/developer include some difficulties with developing material properly, a limited choice of media availability, necessity for more frequent revisions, more trainee preparation needed, increased development time, more difficulty selling concepts, and greater control needs. Anticipated difficulties for employers include higher costs of production, reproduction, distribution, and revision, and possible logistics problems in implementation.

Self-directed instructional programs may involve paper-and-pencil, computer-based, and/or audio-visual formats. In 1991 Porter reported a study of three methods of continuing education for paramedics—lecture, videotape, and computer-assisted instruction-and compared their relative abilities to promote knowledge acquisition and retention. He also examined subject attitude toward each method initially and any changes in attitude immediately after and 60 days after the method. He found that although lecture was the preferred method, computer-assisted instruction was best able to impart knowledge and enhance participant knowledge retention. MacFadven, Brown, Schoenwald, and Feldman (1993) assessed the efficacy of computer-assisted instruction in teaching pharmacokinetics, reportedly a difficult subject to teach, as a part of the clinical pharmacology curriculum for undergraduate medical students. They compared teaching by computer-assisted tutorials to traditional lectures and found that, given an equivalent time commitment, the extent of new learning was not affected by the instructional method used. They feel, however, that depending on the availability of faculty and institutional resources, the greater degree of student acceptance they found favors the broader implementation of computer-assisted tutorials as a replacement of traditional methods of instruction in pharmacokinetics.

A paper-and-pencil self-directed instructional program on anxiety disorders in persons with mental retardation is included in the appendix of this volume. Educational objectives, pre- and post- test questions and answers, and references are included. If this program is utilized for training, a copy of the <u>DSM-IV</u> (1994) should be made available for reference. (This same program is available in computer-assisted format from the author/developer.)

Piskurich (1993) describes an interesting, somewhat informal self-directed learning system for management development which included a series of articles culled from management journals. Objectives and quizzes were added to the articles to make them into instructional packages. This certainly could be done for staff training on any kind of appropriate issue, particularly clinical psychiatric issues.

After individuals have acquired a basic knowledge of diagnostic criteria of anxiety disorders and manifestations of these conditions in persons with mental retardation, introduction of more advanced materials, even those designed for mental health care professionals, may be of value. The American Psychiatric Association has recently introduced videotapes discussing complex clinical issues associated with various psychiatric diagnoses, each of which includes several patient interviews. One of these (Skodol, 1995) discusses anxiety disorders. While this material does not specifically address issues of mental health problems experienced by persons with mental retardation, many of the points stressed may be of interest to those who work with this population. Objectives and quizzes could be readily developed for this type material, thus broadening self-directed instructional offerings in this topic.

References

American Psychiatric Association. (1994). *Diagnostic and statistical manual of mental disorders* (Fourth Ed.). Washington, DC: Author.

King, B. H., DeAntonio, C., McCracken, J. T., Forness, S. R., & Ackerland, V. (1994). Psychiatric consultation in severe and profound mental retardation. *American Journal of Psychiatry, 151,* 1802-1808.

MacFadven, J. C., Brown, J. E., Schoenwald, R., & Feldman, R. D. (1993). The effectiveness of teaching clinical pharmacokinetics by computer. *Clinical Pharmacology and Therapeutics, 53,* 617-621.

Piskurich, G. M. (1993). *Self-directed learning: A practical guide to design, development, and implementation.* San Francisco, CA: Jossey-Bass.

Porter, R. S. (1991). Efficacy of computer-assisted instruction in the continuing education of paramedics. *Annals of Emergency Medicine, 20,* 380-384.

Skodol, A. E. (Discussant) & Alger, I. (Ed.). (1995). *Anxiety disorders: New diagnostic Issues* (Videotape). (Available from American Psychiatric Press, Inc., Washington, DC).

Smoot, S. L. & Gonzales, J. L. (1995). Cost-effective communication skills training for state hospital employees. *Psychiatric Services, 46,* 819-822.

APPENDIX

Definition of Panic Attack, which can occur in a variety of Anxiety Disorders:

(Note: A Panic Attack is not a codable disorder. Code the specific diagnosis in which the Panic Attack occurs.)

A discrete period of intense fear or discomfort, in which at least four of the following symptoms developed abruptly and reached a peak within 10 minutes:

1) palpitations, pounding heart, or accelerated heart rate
2) sweating
3) trembling or shaking
4) sensations of shortness of breath or smothering
5) feeling of choking
6) chest pain or discomfort
7) nausea or abdominal distress
8) feeling dizzy, unsteady, lightheaded, or faint
9) derealization (feelings of unreality) or depersonalization (being detached from oneself)
10) fear of losing control or going crazy
11) fear of dying
12) paresthesias (numbness or tingling sensations)
13) chills or hot flushes

Reference:
Diagnostic and Statistical Manual of Mental Disorders, Fourth Edition (DSM-IV), American Psychiatric Association, Washington, DC, 1994. (Used by permission.)

DIAGNOSTIC CRITERIA FOR GENERALIZED ANXIETY DISORDER, (includes OVERANXIOUS DISORDER OF CHILDHOOD)

A. Excessive anxiety and worry (apprehensive expectation), occurring more days than not for at least six months, about a number of events or activities (such as work or school performance).

B. The person finds it difficult to control the worry.

C. The anxiety and worry are associated with at least three of the following six symptoms (with at least some symptoms present for more days than not for the past six months):
   (Note: Only one item is required in children.)

   1) restlessness or feeling keyed up or on edge
   2) being easily fatigued
   3) difficulty concentrating or mind going blank
   4) irritability
   5) muscle tension
   6) sleep disturbance (difficulty falling or staying asleep, or restless unsatisfying sleep)

D. The focus of the anxiety and worry is not confined to features of an Axis I disorder, e.g., the anxiety or worry is not about having a Panic Attack (as in Panic Disorder), being embarrassed in public (as in Social Phobia), being contaminated (as in Obsessive-Compulsive Disorder), being away from home or close relatives (as in Separation Anxiety Disorder), gaining weight (as in Anorexia Nervosa), having multiple physical complaints (as in Somatization Disorder), or having a serious illness (as in Hypochondriasis),and the anxiety and worry do not occur exclusively during Posttraumatic Stress Disorder.

E. The anxiety, worry, or physical symptoms cause clinically significant distress or impairment in social, occupational, or other important areas of functioning.

F. Not due to the direct physiological effects of a substance (e.g., a drug of abuse, a medication) or a general medical condition (e.g., hyperthyroidism) and does not occur exclusively during a Mood Disorder, Psychotic Disorder, or a Pervasive Developmental Disorder.

Reference:
Diagnostic and Statistical Manual of Mental Disorders, Fourth Edition (DSM-IV), American Psychiatric Association, Washington, DC, 1994. (Used by permission.)

DIAGNOSTIC CRITERIA FOR OBSESSIVE COMPULSIVE DISORDER

A. Either obsessions or compulsions
Obsessions as defined by 1), 2), 3), and 4):
1) recurrent and persistent thoughts, impulses, or images that are experienced, at some time during the disturbance, as intrusive and inappropriate, and cause marked anxiety or distress

2) the thoughts, impulses, or images are not simply excessive worries about real-life problems

3) the person attempts to ignore or suppress such thoughts, impulses, or images, or to neutralize them with some other thought or action

4) the person recognizes that the obsessional thoughts,impulses, or images are a product of his or her own ,mind (not imposed from without as in thought insertion)

Compulsions as defined by 1) and 2):
1) repetitive behaviors (e.g., handwashing, ordering, or checking) or mental acts (e.g., praying, counting, repeating words silently) that the person feels driven to perform in response to an obsession, or according to rules that must be applied rigidly

2) the behaviors or mental acts are aimed at preventing or reducing distress or preventing some dreaded event or situation; however these behaviors or mental acts either are not connected in a realistic way with what they are designed to neutralize or prevent, or are clearly excessive

B. At some point during the course of the disorder, the person has recognized that the obsessions or compulsions are excessive or unreasonable. Note: this does not apply to children.

C. The obsessions or compulsions cause marked distress; are time-consuming (take more than an hour a day), or significantly interfere with the person's normal routine, occupational (or academic) functioning, or usual social activities or relationships.

D. If another Axis I disorder is present, the content of the obsessions or compulsions is not restricted to it (e.g., preoccupation with food in the presence of an Eating Disorder; hair pulling in the presence of Trichotillomania,concern with appearance in the presence of Body Dysmorphic Disorder; preoccupation with drugs in the presence of a Substance Use Disorder; preoccupation with having a serious illness in the presence of Hypochondriasis; preoccupation with sexual urges or fantasies in the presence of a Paraphilia; or guilty ruminations in the presence of Major Depressive Disorder).

E. Not due to the direct physiological effects of a substance (e.g., a drug of abuse, a medication) or a general medical condition.

Specify if Poor Insight Type: if, for most of the time during the current episode, the person does not recognize that the obsessions and compulsions are excessive or unreasonable

Reference: Diagnostic and Statistical Manual of Mental Disorders, Fourth Edition (DSM-IV), American Psychiatric Association, Washington, DC, 1994. (Used by permission.)

DIAGNOSTIC CRITERIA FOR POST-TRAUMATIC STRESS DISORDER

A. The person has been exposed to a traumatic event in which both of the following were present:

1) the person experienced, witnessed, or was confronted with an event or events that involved actual or threatened death or serious injury, or

a threat to the physical integrity of oneself or others

2) the person's response involved intense fear,helplessness, or horror. Note: in children, this may be expressed instead by disorganized or agitated behavior

B. The traumatic event is persistently reexperienced in at least one of the following ways:

1) recurrent and intrusive distressing recollections of the event, including images, thoughts, or perceptions.
Note: in young children, repetitive play may occur in which themes or aspects of the trauma are expressed

2) recurrent distressing dreams of the event. Note: in children, there may be frightening dreams without recognizable content

3) acting or feeling as if the traumatic event were recurring (includes a sense of reliving the experience, illusions, hallucinations, and dissociative flashback episodes, including those that occur upon awakening or when intoxicated) Note: in young children, trauma-specific reenactment may occur

4) intense psychological distress at exposure to internal or external cues that symbolize or resemble an aspect of the traumatic event

5) physiological reactivity on exposure to internal or external cues that symbolize or resemble an aspect of the traumatic event

C. Persistent avoidance of stimuli associated with the trauma and numbing of general responsiveness (not present before the trauma), as indicated by at least three of the following:

1) efforts to avoid thoughts, feelings, or conversations associated with the trauma

2) efforts to avoid activities, places, or people that arouse recollections of the trauma

3) inability to recall an important aspect of the trauma

4) markedly diminished interest or participation in significant activities

5) feeling of detachment or estrangement from others

6) restricted range of affect (e.g., unable to have loving feelings)

7) sense of a foreshortened future (e.g., does not expect to have a career, marriage, children, or a normal life span)

D. Persistent symptoms of increased arousal (not present before the trauma), as indicated by at least two of the following:

1) difficulty falling or staying asleep

2) irritability or outbursts of anger

3) difficulty concentrating

4) hypervigilance

5) exaggerated startle response

E. Duration of the disturbance (symptoms in B, C, and D) is more than one month.

F. The disturbance causes clinically significant distress or impairment in social, occupational, or other important areas of functioning.

Reference: <u>Diagnostic and Statistical Manual of Mental Disorders, Fourth Edition (DSM-IV)</u>, American Psychiatric Association, Washington, DC, 1994. (Used by permission.)

DIAGNOSTIC CRITERIA FOR ANXIETY DISORDER
DUE TO GENERAL MEDICAL CONDITION

A. Prominent anxiety, Panic Attacks, or obsessions or compulsions predominate in the clinical picture.

B. There is evidence from the history, physical examination or laboratory findings that the disturbance is the direct physiological consequence of a general medical condition.

C. The disturbance is not better accounted for by another mental disorder (e.g., Adjustment Disorder With Anxiety in which the stressor is a serious medical condition).

D. The disturbance does not occur exclusively during the course of a delirium.

E. The disturbance causes clinically significant distress or impairment in social, occupational, or other important areas of functioning.

Specify if:

With Generalized Anxiety: if excessive anxiety or worry about a number of events or activities predominates in the clinical presentation

With Panic Attacks: if Panic Attacks predominate in the clinical presentation

With Obsessive-Compulsive Symptoms: if obsessions or compulsions predominate in the clinical presentation

Reference: Diagnostic and Statistical Manual of Mental Disorders, Fourth Edition (DSM-IV), American Psychiatric Association, Washington, DC, 1994. (Used by permission.)

ANXIETY DISORDERS IN PERSONS
WITH MENTAL RETARDATION

Educational objectives for self-directed instructional program on anxiety disorders in persons with mental retardation:

Participants will be able to answer the following questions:
1. What are the most common types of anxiety disorders found both in the general population and in persons with mental retardation?
2. What diagnostic criteria are needed to make a diagnosis of an anxicty disorder?
3. What types of treatment are usually effective for persons with an anxiety disorder?
4. What are common side effects for medications commonly prescribed for anxiety disorders?
5. How can direct support staff and other members of interdisciplinary teams serving persons with mental retardation facilitate diagnosis and treatment of anxiety disorders in this population?

ANXIETY DISORDERS IN PERSONS WITH MENTAL RETARDATION

Pretest/Posttest

T F 1. Anxiety disorders are uncommon in the general population, and are infrequently seen by non-psychiatrist physicians.

T F 2. The term "derealization" defines a sensation that the immediate environment is strange, unreal, or unfamiliar.

T F 3. Symptoms of a panic attack may be mistaken for a heart attack or other serious health problem.

T F 4. Agoraphobia is a technical term which means anxiety about being in places or situations from which escape may be difficult or embarrassing.

T F 5. Symptoms of hyperthyroidism (overactive thyroid gland) may be very similar to those of panic disorder.

T F 6. Trivial fears about flying, involving only tightly gripping armrests on takeoff and landing, meet criteria for a phobic disorder.

T F 7. Individuals with generalized anxiety disorder seldom have difficulty concentrating.

T F 8. Some kinds of asthma medicine cause symptoms similar to those of generalized anxiety disorder.

T F 9. Obsessive compulsive disorder (OCD) is an anxiety disorder in which both obsessions and compulsions must be present.

T F 10. A compulsion is a repetitive behavior or mental act that the person feels drive to perform in response to an obsession or according to rigid rules.

T F 11. A person who is a "worrier" who continually talks about problems they have with their children does not meet criteria for obsessive compulsive disorder.

T F 12. To technically be considered time-consuming, obsessions/compulsions must take at least one hour/day.

T F 13. Post-traumatic stress disorder is an anxiety disorder in which the involved person has been exposed to a severely traumatic event in which his/her response has involved intense fear, helplessness, or horror.

T F 14. When compulsive activity is interrupted in a person with mental retardation, he/she seldom becomes aggressive.

T F 15. Frightening, intrusive thoughts about an experienced auto wreck may represent post-traumatic stress disorder.

T F 16. An individual with mental retardation who always keeps his back to the wall when he is in a room with others is said to be showing "hypervigilance," which may be a symptom of post-traumatic stress disorder.

T F 17. A diagnosis of post-traumatic stress disorder may be made after one weeks' worth of symptoms.

T F 18. Goal of treatment of anxiety disorders is to reduce any symptoms to a manageable level.

T F 19. The commonest side effect of benzodiazepine drugs such as Valium, Ativan, and Xanax, is over-excitement.

T F 20. Everyone with a diagnosis of anxiety disorder requires drug treatment.

Name:_____

Position:_____

Date:_____

Answers to Pretest/Posttest on Anxiety Disorders:

1. False
2. True
3. True
4. True
5. True
6. False
7. False
8. True
9. False
10. True
11. True
12. True
13. True
14. False
15. True
16. True
17. False
18. True
19. False
20. False

ANXIETY DISORDERS IN PERSONS WITH MENTAL RETARDATION

Instructions for use of this self-directed instruction program:

Cover the right-hand side of each page, since this gives the answer.

Read each section carefully, and WRITE your answer in the designated place.

After WRITING your answer, check and see if you are correct.

ANXIETY DISORDERS IN PERSONS WITH MENTAL RETARDATION

ANXIETY DISORDERS are the most common mental health disorders seen by primary care physicians. The typical primary care physician sees at least one patient with an anxiety disorder every day. The characteristic features of this group of disorders include symptoms of ANXIETY and AVOIDANCE behavior. Anxiety disorders are (common or relatively rare?).

common

_____

While depression and anxiety disorders have some symptoms in common, and may occur in the same individual, features more characteristic of anxiety include difficulty falling asleep, avoidance behavior based on fear, rapid pulse, breathing difficulties, apprehension, tremors, heart palpitations, sweating, hot or cold spells, & dizziness. Sleep disorders associated with anxiety usually include _____ _____ _____.

difficulty falling asleep.
(The usual sleep disorder pattern seen in depression in adults is early awakening.)

Another symptom often associated with anxiety disorders is the feeling of detachment from all or parts of one's body (depersonalization). The technical term for feeling of detachment from one's own body parts is

_____.

depersonalization

Yet another symptom often associated with various anxiety disorders is the sensation that the immediate environment is strange, unreal, or unfamiliar (derealization). The technical term for the sensation that the current environment is unfamiliar or strange is

_____.

derealization

A PANIC ATTACK can occur in a variety of anxiety disorders. This is not a diagnosis, but is a group of symptoms which occur during a discrete period of intense fear or discomfort. The Diagnostic andStatistical Manual of Mental Disorders, Fourth Edition (DSM-IV) lists 13 of these symptoms, four of which must be present, develop abruptly, and reach a peak within 10 minutes. A panic attack involves the presence of at least _____ of 13 symptoms, starting abruptly.

four

Among listed symptoms of a panic attack are 1) palpitations, 2) sweating, 3) trembling or shaking, 4) shortness of breath or sensation of smothering, 5) feeling of choking, 6) chest pain or discomfort, & 7) nausea or abdominal distress. Symptoms of panic attack which may be mistaken for a heart attack include palpitations, shortness of breath, and c_____ _____.

chest pain

Other listed symptoms of a panic attack include 8) feeling dizzy or lightheaded, 9) derealization (feelings of unreality) or depersonalization (feeling detached from oneself), 10) fear of losing control or going crazy, 11) fear of dying, 12) paresthesias (numbness or tingling sensations), and 13) chills or hot flushes. The technical term for sensations of numbness or tingling is _____.

paresthesias

AGORAPHOBIA means anxiety about being in places or situations from which escape might be difficult or embarrassing, or in which help might not be available in the event of having an unexpected panic attack. An individual who refuses to leave his/her home because of fear of a panic attack is said to have a condition called _____.

agoraphobia

To make a diagnosis of panic disorder without agora-phobia, recurrent, unexpected panic attacks must be present, and at least one attack should be followed by a month or more of persistent concern about having more attacks, worry about implications of the attack or its consequences, and/or a significant behavior change related to the attacks. To make a diagnosis of panic disorder without agoraphobia, at least one attack must be followed by ____ month's other symptoms.

one (or more)

Other conditions such as effects of some prescribed drugs, drugs of abuse, or hyperthyroidism (excessive thyroid function) may present with symptoms similar to those symptoms of a panic attack. Symptoms of hyperthyroidism (may be mistaken for or are quite dissimilar to?) panic disorder.._____

may be mistaken for

SPECIFIC PHOBIA is defined as a marked and persistent fear of a specific object or situation. Examples are fear of flying, heights, animals, receiving an injection, and seeing blood. Exposure to the specific object or situation almost always provokes an immediate anxiety response, which often takes the form of a panic attack which is bound or predisposed to the situation. A person who has a dog phobia may have a p_____ _____ when he/she sees a dog.

panic attack

In children, panic associated with a phobia may be expressed by crying, tantrums, freezing, or clinging. Persons with mental retardation may react in similar fashion, or may become aggressive to get away from the feared situation. Adults with phobias recognize that the fear is excessive or unreasonable, but this feature may be absent in persons with mental retardation or children. Phobic adults (recognize or seldom recognize?) that their fear is irrational. _____

recognize

In a true phobia, the avoidance, anxious anticipation or distress in the feared situations interferes significantly with normal routine, functioning, social activities, or relationships with others, or there is marked distress about having the phobia. Trivial fears about flying, involving only the tight gripping of the armrests on take-off and landing, (meet or do not meet?) criteria for a phobic disorder. _____

do not meet

Many persons with anxiety have GENERALIZED ANXIETY DISORDER, in which they have excessive anxiety and worry about a number of events or activities, occurring more days than not, for at least six months. The individual with generalized anxiety disorder finds it difficult to control his/her worry. The worry associated with generalized anxiety disorder is (difficult or easy?) for the affected individual to control. _____

difficult

Symptoms which may be associated with generalized anxiety disorder include restlessness, easy fatiguability, difficulty concentrating, irritability, muscle tension, and sleep disturbance (difficulty falling or staying asleep,or restless, unsatisfying sleep). Individuals with generalized anxiety disorder (often or seldom?) have trouble concentrating. _____

often

The anxiety, worry, or physical symptoms of generalized anxiety disorder cause clinically significant distress or impairment in social, occupational, or other important areas of functioning. Some medications, such as asthma medications, can cause symptoms similar to anxiety disorders, as do some general medical conditions such as over-active thyroid gland. Some kinds of asthma medicine (do or do not?) cause symptoms similar to those of generalized anxiety disorder._____

do

Obsessive compulsive disorder (OCD) is an anxiety disorder in which either obsessions or compulsions must be present. OBSESSIONS are defined as recurrent and persistent thoughts, impulses, or images that are experienced, at some time during disturbance, as intrusive and inappropriate, marked anxiety or distress. Recurrent, persistent thoughts that cause distress or anxiety, and are recognized as inappropriate are called _____.

obsessions (Children or persons with the mental and cause retardation may not be able to recognize and/or describe these as inappropriate.)

Thoughts, impulses, or images associated with obsessions are not simply excessive worries about real-life problems. The affected individual attempts to ignore or suppress these thoughts or images, or tries to neutralize them with some other thought or action. A person who is a "worrier who continually talks about problems they have with their children (meets or does not meet?) criteria for obsessive compulsive disorder._____

does not meet

A person with obsessive compulsive disorder recognizes that the obsessional thoughts, impulses, or images are a product of his/her own mind, and not imposed from without. Children or persons with mental retardation may not show this symptom. An individual who feels that he must wash his hands continuously because God is telling him he is unclean (meets or does not meet?) criteria for obsessive compulsive disorder.

_____

does not meet

COMPULSIONS are defined as repetitive behaviors (such as handwashing, ordering, checking) or mental acts (praying, counting) that the person feels driven to perform in response to an obsession, or according to rigid rules. These rules or behaviors are aimed at preventing or reducing distress or preventing some dreaded event or situation, but are not connected in a realistic way to that distress, or are excessive. Compulsions are (repetitive or occasional?) acts. _____

repetitive

At some point during the course of OCD, the person has recognized that the obsessions and/or compulsions are excessive or unreasonable. This does not necessarily apply to children or persons with mental retardation. The obsessions and/or compulsions cause marked distress, are time-consuming (more than an hour a day), or interfere with the person's normal routine. To be considered time- consuming, obsessions/compulsions must take at least ____ hour/day.

one

Dr. A. Gedye has developed the COMPULSIVE BEHAVIOR CHECKLIST for use with people with developmental disabilities. It lists 25 types of compulsions "done" by adults with developmental disabilities. This checklist does not make a diagnosis of OCD, but was designed for use by consultants in inter staff members. The Compulsive Behavior Checklist (makes the diagnosis or only assists in gathering information to make am diagnosis?) _____

only assists in gathering information to make a diagnosis

In Dr. Gedye's Compulsive Behavior Checklist, the 25 types of "compulsions" are grouped into five categories: Ordering Compulsions, Completeness/Incompleteness Compulsions, Cleaning/Tidiness Compulsions, Checking/Touching Compulsions, and Deviant Grooming Compulsions. The Compulsive Behavior Checklist, designed for use in quantifying numbers and types of compulsive behavior in persons with mental retardation, has_____ general categories.

five

ORDERING COMPULSIONS include arranging objects in certain patterns, arranging items in one spot,wanting chairs in a fixed arrangement, wanting/arranging peers to sit in certain chairs, using the same chair or location when in a particular room, and insisting on doing a certain activity at the same time of day. An individual who arranges his dresser items neatly in a certain pattern every day and becomes upset when these are moved has a(n) _____compulsion.

ordering

COMPLETENESS/INCOMPLETENESS compulsions include insisting on closing open doors, taking all items out of a storage area, removing items and then returning them (over and over), trying to empty all toiletry bottles in bathroom, putting on and taking off clothing over and over, and insisting on doing a certain chore (not letting anyone else do it). Counting these kinds of behaviors in a person with mental retardation (may help in or doesn't help in?) making an OCD diagnosis.

may help in

CLEANING/TIDINESS compulsions include insisting on doing hygiene steps in a fixed sequence, cleaning body parts excessively, insisting on picking up stray bits off the ground, picking at loose threads continuously, ripping clothes if not prevented, insisting that a certain activity be done, and hiding or hoarding particular objects. an individual who continuously picks at clothing until it tears appears to have a(n) _____ compulsion.

cleaning/tidiness

CHECKING/TOUCHING compulsions include opening a cupboard door and then reclosing it over and over, touching or tapping an item repeatedly, going through a touching or stepping pattern, or doing unusual sniffing. (Some people with autism appear to go through some of these same rituals.) Common checking/touching compulsions include all but which one of the following: stepping in repeated patterns, repeatedly opening and closing a door, arranging items neatly?

arranging items neatly (over and over!)

DEVIANT GROOMING compulsions include picking at face/hands/legs etc. to the point of gouging skin, checking self in a mirror excessively, inappropriate hair cutting, pulling at hair, and pulling out hair when sitting calmly. Skin damage (may result from or probably doesn't result from?) a deviant grooming compulsion. _____

may result from

After some count of the types of compulsions and the number of categories (obsessions) evidenced by a person with mental retardation, some assessment of the amount of interference with daily living should be made, particularly whether or not the compulsions take more than one hour/day if not prevented, and whether or not they significantly interfere with the person's normal routine. Interference with daily living (is or isn't?) important in an analysis. _____

is

Another important part of the Compulsive Behavior Checklist involves measure of response of the involved individual to staff interruption of compulsions. Examples include halting momentarily, then resuming activity; waiting until caretaker is gone, then resuming; becoming angry and aggressive against staff who intervenes; biting or hitting self; or headbanging. When compulsive activity is interrupted in a person with mental retardation, he/she may get (aggressive or cooperative?)_____

aggressive

Post-traumatic stress disorder is an anxiety disorder in which the involved person has been exposed to a traumatic event in which both of the following were present: experiencing, witnessing, or being confronted with a situation that involved actual or threatened death or serious injury, to self or others, plus the individual's response involved intense fear helplessness, or horror. An individual who comes close to death by fire may experience _____.

post-traumatic stress disorder

In post-traumatic stress disorder the traumatic event is persistently re-experienced in at least one of the following ways: recurrent and intrusive recollections of the event, recurrent distressing dreams of the event, acting or feeling as if the event were recurring, intense psychological distress to cues symbolizing the event, & physical symptoms on exposure to cues of the event. Frightening, intrusive thoughts of an experienced car wreck may represent _____.

post-traumatic stress disorder (PTSD)

Persons with PTSD have persistent avoidance of stimuli associated with the trauma, and have numbing of general responsiveness. These symptoms may present as efforts to avoid thoughts, feelings, or conversations associated with the trauma, efforts to avoid situations or people that cause memories of the trauma, and/or inability to recall facts about the trauma. An individual with PTSD may (avoid or seek out?) activities that arouse memories of the trauma. _____

avoid

Other manifestations of PTSD may include decreased interest or participation in significant activities, feelings of detachment or estrangement from others, inability to have loving feelings, and/or a sense of a foreshortened future (not expecting to have a normal life span). Persons with post-traumatic stress disorder often have (much or very little?) hope for a long and happy life. _____

very little

The initials "PTSD" stand for one of the anxiety disorders, _____.

post-traumatic stress disorder

Individuals with PTSD have persistent symptoms of increased arousal such as difficulty falling or staying asleep, irritability or outbursts of anger, difficulty concentrating, hypervigilance, and/or exaggerated startle response. An individual with mental retardation always keeps his back to the wall when he is in a room with others, and watches everyone around closely. This is an example of h_____, which may be a symptom of PTSD.

| | hypervigilance |

To make a diagnosis of post-traumatic stress disorder, the duration of the disturbance must be more than one month, and the disturbance must cause clinically significant distress or impair ment in important areas of functioning. If an individual has occasional bad dreams about an auto accident, but otherwise seems okay, he probably (does or does not?) have PTSD.

| | does not |

Most types of anxiety disorders are long-term problems. The goal of ANY kind(s) of treatment is to decrease symptoms to a manageable level. Total elimination of symptoms may not be possible. When persons have relatively mild symptoms, usually related to stress, nonpharmacologic (non-drug) treatments usually are satisfactory and should be tried first. Drug therapy (is or is not?) indicated for every case of anxiety disorder.

| | is not |

If symptoms of anxiety disorders are especially severe or persistent, some combination of drugs and non-drug treatments may be required. In treatment, physical causes of anxiety symptoms should be ruled out FIRST. Then, any connections with daily activities and life circumstances should be carefully explored. The first step in management of anxiety symptoms is evaluation of possible _____ causes.

| | physical |

Next, life circumstances and daily activities that seem to be contributing to symptoms of anxiety are corrected or modified if that is possible. Life circumstances that cause an individual to experience anxiety can (always, never, or some times?) be corrected or at least modified to help improve symptoms. _____

sometimes

After physical causes (such as effects of medication and thyroid disorder) are ruled out, and possible corrections of life circumstances are made, other treatments such as learning relaxation techniques or biofeedback may be attempted. Relaxation techniques (often or seldom?) are beneficial for people with anxiety disorders._____

often

Exercise may be beneficial for many persons with Generalized Anxiety Disorder, and often is a part of an overall treatment plan. Biofeedback, relaxation training, and e_____ are commonly used parts of treatment for persons with anxiety disorders.

exercise

The most effective form of treatment for most people with simple phobias is graduated exposure to the feared situation. As an example, a person who is very afraid of heights might first practice looking through a closed window 50 feet above the ground, then as he/she becomes comfortable with that, gradually working to standing on an open balcony. A person with a dog phobia (may or probably doesn't?) need to practice looking first at dogs that are far away. _____

may (Exposure programs should consist of "real life" exposure to the feared object or situation rather than just to a picture.)

Fear of air travel is a very common simple phobia, for which people often seek treatment. Graduated practice is particularly difficult in case of fear of flying, since the affected individual cannot leave the feared situation once the airplane takes off. People with severe fear of flying, when required to fly, may require _____.

medication

Benzodiazepine drugs such as Librium, Valium, Tranxene, Centrax, Paxipam, Serax, Ativan, and Xanax (all trade names) are the commonest drugs prescribed for the treatment of anxiety disorders. The most common side effect for this group of drugs is drowsiness, but some individuals develop a DISINHIBITING reaction. This reaction is more common in persons with mental retardation than for others. The commonest side effect of benzodiazepines is _____.

drowsiness
(sedation)

Some physical dependence usually occurs if individuals receive benzodiazepine drugs for a prolonged period of time. Incidence of dependence and sedation varies from preparation to preparation. Xanax, among the least sedating of any of these drugs, is said to have the most potential for development of physical dependence. While prolonged treatment with Xanax may lead to physical dependence, Xanax is less apt to cause _____ than other drugs in the group.

drowsiness
(sedation)

An individual with mental retardation and some symptoms of anxiety becomes more restless and appears "silly" after her Ativan dosage is increased. This may be an example of a d_____ reaction to a benzodiazepine drug.

disinhibiting
(If continued increases are made, she may get worse.)

BuSpar (buspirone) is a relatively new, non-sedating antianxiety drug that is NOT a benzodiazepine. Side effects are uncommon, but may include headache, nausea, dizziness, and tension. Therapeutic effects of BuSpar take several weeks to develop, while the therapeutic effects of the benzodiazepine drugs are immediate. The therapeutic effects of Valium and Ativan can be expected to be (immediate or delayed?)

immediate

Several antidepressant drugs, not usually used for anxiety disorders, seem to be particularly effective for obsessive compulsive disorders. These drugs seem to increase levels of one of the brain chemical messengers, serotonin. Anafranil (clomipramine) is a tricyclic drug whose side effects include dry mouth, weight gain, and constipation. Side effects of Anafranil might be expected to include ALL BUT dry mouth, diarrhea, or weight gain? _____

diarrhea

Another antidepressant drug commonly used for obsessive compulsive disorder is Prozac (fluoxitine), whose common side effects includedry mouth, dizziness, weight loss, low blood sodium, and low blood sugar. Prozac is associated with (weight gain or weight loss?). _____

weight loss
(possibly)

Persons with mental retardation may have problems with symptoms of anxiety just as do other persons. Direct support staff who are knowledgeable about the signs and symptoms of anxiety disorders are of vital importance in making a diagnosis in this group of persons so that appropriate treatment programs can be developed and implemented. Direct support staff and others who know an individual with mental retardation well are of (vital or very little?) help in making a diagnosis. _____

vital (!!)

Please address questions and comments to:

Ann R. Poindexter, M.D.
1024 Clifton Street
Conway, AR 72032
(501) 329-8488
FAX (501) 336-9831

References for self-directed instructional program on Anxiety Disorders:

Gedye, A. (1992). Recognizing obsessive-compulsive disorder in clients with developmental disabilities. *The Habilitative Mental Healthcare Newsletter, 11*, 73-77.

Gilman, A. G., Rall, T. W., Nies, A. S., & Taylor, P. (Eds.) (1990). *Goodman and Gilman's The pharmacological basis of therapeutics* (8th ed.). New York: Pergamon Press.

Hurst, D. F. & Kaupa, P. A. (1994). A dual approach to treating panic disorder. *Family Practice Recertification, 16*, 49-62.

Leaman, T. L. (1993). Anxiety disorders: Reaching the untreated. *The Female Patient, 18*, 99-102.

McGlynn, T. J. & Metcalf, H. L. (eds.) (1989). *Diagnosis and treatment of anxiety disorders: A physician's handbook*. Washington, DC: American Psychiatric Press.

INDEX

104